English Language Arts
Activity Book

5

Book Staff and Contributors

Kristen Kinney-Haines *Director, English Language Arts*
Amy Rauen *Director, Instructional Design*
Mary Beck Desmond *Senior Text Editor*
Allyson Jacob *Text Editor*
Tricia Battipede *Senior Creative Manager*
Julie Jankowski *Senior Visual Designer*
Caitlin Gildrien *Visual Designer*
Sheila Smith *Print Designer*
Tricia Battipede, Mike Bohman, Shannon Palmer *Cover Designers*
Robyn Campbell, Heather Evans, Alane Gernon-Paulsen, Tara Gleason, Tim Mansfield, Melisa Rice, Tisha Ruibal *Writers*
Amy Eward *Content Specialist; Senior Manager, Writers and Editors*
Dan Smith *Senior Project Manager*

Doug McCollum *Senior Vice President, Product Development*
Kristin Morrison *Vice President, Design, Creative, and User Experience*
Rohit Lakhani *Vice President, Program Management and Operations*
Kelly Engel *Senior Director, Curriculum*
Christopher Frescholtz *Senior Director, Program Management*
Erica Castle *Director, Creative Services*
Lisa Dimaio Iekel *Senior Production Manager*

Illustrations Credits

All illustrations © Stride, Inc. unless otherwise noted
Characters: Tommy DiGiovanni, Matt Fedor, Ben Gamache, Shannon Palmer
Cover: Dolphin © brulove/Shutterstock; Spiral © Silmen/iStock

At Stride, Inc. (NYSE: LRN)—formerly K12 Inc.—we are reimagining lifelong learning as a rich, deeply personal experience that prepares learners for tomorrow. Since its inception, Stride has been committed to removing barriers that impact academic equity and to providing high-quality education for anyone—particularly those in underserved communities. The company has transformed the teaching and learning experience for millions of people by providing innovative, high-quality, tech-enabled education solutions, curriculum, and programs directly to students, schools, the military, and enterprises in primary, secondary, and post-secondary settings. Stride is a premier provider of K-12 education for students, schools, and districts, including career learning services through middle and high school curriculum. Providing a solution to the widening skills gap in the workplace and student loan crisis, Stride equips students with real world skills for in-demand jobs with career learning. For adult learners, Stride delivers professional skills training in healthcare and technology, as well as staffing and talent development for Fortune 500 companies. Stride has delivered millions of courses over the past decade and serves learners in all 50 states and more than 100 countries. The company is a proud sponsor of the Future of School, a nonprofit organization dedicated to closing the gap between the pace of technology and the pace of change in education. More information can be found at stridelearning.com, K12.com, destinationsacademy.com, galvanize.com, techelevator.com, and medcerts.com.

Copyright © 2021, 2019 Stride, Inc. All rights reserved. Stride and the Stride logo, K12 and the K12 logo are trademarks or registered trademarks of Stride, Inc. or its affiliates in the U.S. and other countries. Other names may be trademarks of third parties.

No part of this document may be reproduced in any form or by any means, graphic, electronic, or mechanical, including but not limited to photocopying, recording, taping, and information retrieval systems, without the prior written permission of Stride, Inc.

ISBN: 978-1-60153-575-7

Printed by Action Printing, Fond du Lac, WI, USA, April 2022.

Table of Contents

Author Study

Author Study (A)
Spelling List 1 Pretest 1

Author Study (A)
Write About Point of View and Theme 3

Author Study (B)
Spelling List 1 Activity Bank 7

Author Study (B)
Write a "What If?" 11

Author Study (C)
Write a Summary of *Sarah, Plain and Tall* 13

Author Study (D)
Compare and Contrast a Character 15

Author Study (E)
Compare and Contrast Settings and Events in Two Stories 17

Author Study Wrap-Up
Write About Texts by Patricia MacLachlan 19

Context Clues and Word Relationships
Apply: Context Clues and Word Relationships 23

Narrative Writing Skills (A)
Spelling List 2 Pretest 25

Narrative Writing Skills (A)
Write What Happens Next 27

Narrative Writing Skills (B)
Spelling List 2 Activity Bank 29

Narrative Writing Skills (B)
Write About Characters and Events 33

Narrative Writing Skills (C)
Write a Conclusion and Revise Your Word Choice 37

Narrative Writing Skills Wrap-Up
Use Narrative Writing Skills 39

Fascinating Tales from History

The Mary Celeste (A)
Spelling List 3 Pretest **43**

The Mary Celeste (A)
Write About the Main Idea and Make Predictions **45**

The Mary Celeste (B)
Spelling List 3 Activity Bank **47**

The Mary Celeste (B)
Write About the Ship's Log **49**

The Mary Celeste (C)
Write a Summary **51**

The Mary Celeste Wrap-Up
Write About *The Mary Celeste* **53**

Narrative Writing: Prewriting (A)
Spelling List 4 Pretest **55**

Narrative Writing: Prewriting (A)
Brainstorm for Your Personal Narrative **57**

Narrative Writing: Prewriting (B)
Spelling List 4 Activity Bank **59**

Narrative Writing: Prewriting (B)
Prewrite for Your Personal Narrative **63**

Narative Writing: Drafting (A)
Draft Your Personal Narrative **65**

Nuance
Apply: Nuance **73**

Mesmerized (A)
Spelling List 5 Pretest **77**

Mesmerized (A)
Write About Franklin and Mesmer **79**

Mesmerized (B)
Spelling List 5 Activity Bank **81**

Mesmerized (B)
Write About Multiple Main Ideas **85**

Mesmerized (C)
Summarize *Mesmerized* **87**

***Mesmerized* Wrap-Up**
  Write About Ben Franklin **89**

A Wonder of the World

Narrative Writing: Revising
  Revise Your Personal Narrative **91**

Narrative Writing: Proofreading
  Proofread Your Personal Narrative **93**

Queen of the Falls
  Spelling List 6 Pretest **95**

Queen of the Falls
  Write About Annie Taylor **97**

***Queen of the Falls* Wrap-Up**
  Spelling List 6 Activity Bank **99**

***Queen of the Falls* Wrap-Up**
  Write About *Queen of the Falls* **103**

***Where Is Niagra Falls?* (A)**
  Write About the Main Ideas of Chapters 3 and 4 .... **105**

***Where Is Niagra Falls?* (B)**
  Write About Viewpoints and Write A Summary **107**

***Where Is Niagra Falls?* Wrap-Up**
  Write About *Where Is Niagra Falls?* **111**

Dictionary Skills
  Apply: More Dictionary Skills Practice **113**

A Wrinkle in Time

Government Words
  Apply: Government Words **117**

***A Wrinkle in Time* (A)**
  Spelling List 7 Pretest **121**

***A Wrinkle in Time* (A)**
  Write About Chapter 1 and Visualize the Text **123**

***A Wrinkle in Time* (B)**
  Spelling List 7 Activity Bank **125**

A Wrinkle in Time (B)
  Write a Summary of Chapters 1–3..**127**

A Wrinkle in Time (C)
  Write About the Text..**129**

A Wrinkle in Time (D)
  Write About Characters..**131**

A Wrinkle in Time (E)
  Spelling List 8 Pretest..**133**

A Wrinkle in Time (E)
  Write About Challenges and Themes..**135**

A Wrinkle in Time (F)
  Spelling List 8 Activity Bank..**137**

A Wrinkle in Time (F)
  Write About Charles Wallace...**141**

A Wrinkle in Time (G)
  Write About Two Settings...**143**

A Wrinkle in Time (H)
  Write About Another Theme..**145**

A Wrinkle in Time (I)
  Write About Chapter 12..**147**

A Wrinkle in Time Wrap-Up
  Write About *A Wrinkle in Time*..**149**

Informational Writing Skills (A)
  Spelling List 9 Pretest..**151**

Informational Writing Skills (A)
  Write About a Celestial Body...**153**

Informational Writing Skills (B)
  Spelling List 9 Activity Bank..**155**

Informational Writing Skills (B)
  Develop Your Topic...**159**

Informational Writing Skills (C)
  Clear Up and Conclude Your Paragraph......................................**161**

Informational Writing Skills Wrap-Up
  Use Informational Writing Skills..**163**

Finding Their Way

Figurative Language
Apply: Comparisons and Sound Words 167

***You Should Meet Katherine Johnson* (A)**
Spelling List 10 Pretest 169

***You Should Meet Katherine Johnson* (A)**
Create a Time Line, Chapters 1–3 171

***You Should Meet Katherine Johnson* (B)**
Spelling List 10 Activity Bank 173

***You Should Meet Katherine Johnson* (B)**
Create a Time Line, Chapters 4–5 177

***You Should Meet Katherine Johnson* (C)**
Write About Katherine Johnson 179

You Should Meet Katherine Johnson
Wrap-Up: Write a Review 181

Informational Writing: Prewriting (A)
Spelling List 11 Pretest 183

Informational Writing: Prewriting (A)
Brainstorm for Your Science Report 185

Informational Writing: Prewriting (B)
Spelling List 11 Activity Bank 189

Informational Writing: Prewriting (B)
Research Your Science Report 191

Informational Writing: Prewriting (C)
Outline for Your Science Report 195

Informational Writing: Drafting (A)
Draft Your Science Report 199

***Hidden Figures* (A)**
Spelling List 12 Pretest 203

***Hidden Figures* (A)**
Write About Miriam Mann 205

***Hidden Figures* (B)**
Spelling List 12 Activity Bank 207

***Hidden Figures* (B)**
Write About *Hidden Figures*, Chapters 10–12 211

Hidden Figures (C)
 Write About Women at NASA Then and Now 213

Hidden Figures Wrap-Up
 Write About Hidden Figures 215

Moments in History

"A Ride in the Night"
 Spelling List 13 Pretest 217

"A Ride in the Night"
 Write About Will Clark 219

"A Ride in the Night" Wrap-Up
 Spelling List 13 Activity Bank 221

"A Ride in the Night" Wrap-Up
 Write About "A Ride in the Night" 225

"Run, Kate Shelley, Run"
 Write About Key Details and Main Ideas 227

"Run, Kate Shelley, Run" Wrap-Up
 Write About "Run, Kate Shelley, Run" 229

Informational Writing: Revising
 Revise Your Science Report 231

Informational Writing: Proofreading
 Proofread Your Science Report 233

Greek Roots and Affixes
 Apply: Greek Roots and Affixes 235

"Young Frederick Douglass"
 Spelling List 14 Pretest 237

"Young Frederick Douglass"
 Write About Multiple Main Ideas 239

"Young Frederick Douglass" Wrap-Up
 Spelling List 14 Activity Bank 241

"Young Frederick Douglass" Wrap-Up
 Write About "Young Frederick Douglass" 245

"The Most Famous Woman in America"
 Write About Facts and Opinions 247

"The Most Famous Woman in America" Wrap-Up
    Write About "The Most Famous Woman in America".................249

Persuasion and Opinion

Microscopes (A)
    Spelling List 15 Pretest.................251

Microscopes (A)
    Write About the Author's Beliefs.................253

Microscopes (B)
    Spelling List 15 Activity Bank.................255

Microscopes (B)
    Paraphrase a Passage.................257

Microscopes (C)
    Plan to Write About Microscopes.................259

Microscopes Wrap-Up
    Write About Microscopes.................263

Latin Roots and Affixes
    Apply: Practice Using Words with Latin Roots.................265

Opinion Writing Skills (A)
    Spelling List 16 Pretest.................267

Opinion Writing Skills (A)
    Begin Your Opinion Piece.................269

Opinion Writing Skills (B)
    Spelling List 16 Activity Bank.................271

Opinion Writing Skills (B)
    Order Reasons and Provide Evidence.................275

Opinion Writing Skills (C)
    Link Ideas and Conclude Your Opinion Piece.................277

Opinion Writing Skills Wrap-Up
    Use Opinion Writing Skills.................279

Solar Power (A)
    Spelling List 17 Pretest.................283

Solar Power (A)
    Write About a Persuasive Passage.................285

Solar Power (B)
   Spelling List 17 Activity Bank 287

Solar Power (B)
   Write About How a Writer Persuades Readers 291

Solar Power (C)
   Plan to Write About Solar Power 293

Solar Power Wrap-Up
   Write About Solar Power 297

Get to Know a Supreme Court Justice

Who Is Sonia Sotomayor? **(A)**
   Spelling List 18 Pretest 301

Who Is Sonia Sotomayor? **(A)**
   Write About Events in Your Biography 303

Who Is Sonia Sotomayor? **(B)**
   Spelling List 18 Activity Bank 305

Who Is Sonia Sotomayor? **(B)**
   Write About Facts and Opinions 309

Who Is Sonia Sotomayor? **(C)**
   Write About Sonia Sotomayor Using Text Features 311

Who Is Sonia Sotomayor? **Wrap-Up**
   Write About *Who Is Sonia Sotomayor?* 313

Sonia Sotomayor's Opening Statement
   Write About What You Learned 315

Sonia Sotomayor's Opening Statement Wrap-Up
   Write About Sonia Sotomayor, Supreme Court Justice 317

Logical Relationships
   Write Sentences with Signal Words.....................................319

Opinion Writing: Prewriting (A)
   Spelling List 19 Pretest 321

Opinion Writing: Prewriting (A)
   Brainstorm for Your Editorial..323

Opinion Writing: Prewriting (B)
   Spelling List 19 Activity Bank 327

Opinion Writing: Prewriting (B)
   Research Your Editorial..329

Opinion Writing: Prewriting (C)
　　Plan Your Editorial 333

Opinion Writing: Drafting (A)
　　Draft Your Editorial 337

Inside Out and Back Again

Homonyms and Homographs
　　Apply: Homonyms and Homographs 343

Inside Out and Back Again **(A)**
　　Spelling List 20 Pretest 345

Inside Out and Back Again **(A)**
　　Write About Visual Elements in Poetry 347

Inside Out and Back Again **(B)**
　　Spelling List 20 Activity Bank 349

Inside Out and Back Again **(B)**
　　Making a Prediction 353

Inside Out and Back Again **(C)**
　　Special Delivery 355

Inside Out and Back Again **(D)**
　　Theme and Character Response 357

Inside Out and Back Again **(E)**
　　Spelling List 21 Pretest 359

Inside Out and Back Again **(E)**
　　Identify Figurative Language 361

Inside Out and Back Again **(F)**
　　Spelling List 21 Activity Bank 363

Inside Out and Back Again **(F)**
　　Plan a Narrative Poem 367

Inside Out and Back Again **(G)**
　　Write a Narrative Poem 371

Inside Out and Back Again **(H)**
　　Revise and Publish a Narrative Poem 375

Inside Out and Back Again **Wrap-Up**
　　Summary of *Inside Out and Back Again* 377

Opinion Writing: Revising
　　Revise Your Editorial... 379

Opinion Writing: Proofreading
　　Proofread Your Editorial 381

Choice Reading Project

Choice Reading Project
　　Spelling List 22 Pretest 383
Choice Reading Project
　　Spelling List 22 Activity Bank 385
Choice Reading Project
　　Spelling List 23 Pretest 389
Choice Reading Project
　　Spelling List 23 Activity Bank 391
Presentation Skills (A)
　　Present Your Opinion 393
Presentation Skills (B)
　　Add Pictures to Your Opinion Speech 395
Presentation Skills Wrap-Up
　　Use Presentation Skills 397
Idioms
　　Apply: Idioms 401

Money

"From Barter to Bitcoin"
　　Spelling List 24 Pretest 403
"From Barter to Bitcoin"
　　Write About Two Ways of Buying Goods 405
"From Barter to Bitcoin"
　　Spelling List 24 Activity Bank 407
"From Barter to Bitcoin" Wrap-Up
　　Write About "From Barter to Bitcoin" 411
"Making Money"
　　Write About a Process 413
"Making Money" Wrap-Up
　　Write About "Making Money" 415
Economy Words
　　Apply: Using Context Clues 417

Presentation: Digital Tools
    Spelling List 25 Pretest 419

Presentation: Digital Tools
    Use Presentation Software 421

Presentation: Planning
    Spelling List 25 Activity Bank 423

Presentation: Planning
    Plan Your Presentation 427

Presentation: Research
    Research Your Presentation 431

"The Value of Money"
    Spelling List 26 Pretest 437

"The Value of Money"
    Write About Two Texts 439

"The Value of Money" Wrap-Up
    Spellling List 26 Activity Bank 441

"The Value of Money" Wrap-Up
    Write About "The Value of Money" 445

"The Future of Money"
    Write About Different Structures 447

"The Future of Money" Wrap-Up
    Write About What You've Read 449

The Adventures of Sherlock Holmes

Sayings
    Apply: Use Common Sayings 451

Meet Sherlock Holmes (A)
    Spelling List 27 Pretest 453

Meet Sherlock Holmes (A)
    Draw a Conclusion 455

Meet Sherlock Holmes (B)
    Spelling List 27 Activity Bank 457

Meet Sherlock Holmes (B)
    Write About a Different Narrator 459

Meet Sherlock Holmes (C)
    Write About the Texts and Make a Prediction 461

Meet Sherlock Holmes (D)
    Write a Summary of the Story 463

Meet Sherlock Holmes (E)
    Spelling List 28 Pretest 465

Meet Sherlock Holmes (E)
    Plan Your Own Graphic Mystery Story 467

Meet Sherlock Holmes (F)
    Spelling List 28 Activity Bank 469

Meet Sherlock Holmes (F)
    Write a Graphic Mystery Story 473

Meet Sherlock Holmes (G)
    Write About Your Reactions..477

Meet Sherlock Holmes (H)
    Write About Listening to a Text 479

Meet Sherlock Holmes Wrap-Up
    Write About Sherlock Holmes 481

Presentation: Revising
    Revise Your Informational Presentation 483

Presentation: Proofreading
    Proofread Your Informational Presentation 485

Presentation: Publishing
    Reflect on Your Informational Presentation 487

Glossary A-1

Author Study (A)

Spelling List 1 Pretest

1. Open the Spelling Pretest activity online. Listen to the first spelling word. Type the word. Check your answer.

2. Write the correct spelling of the word in the Word column of the Spelling Pretest table on the next page.

	Word	✓	✗
1	blindfold		

3. Put a check mark in the ✓ column if you spelled the word correctly online.

	Word	✓	✗
1	blindfold	✓	

Put an X in the ✗ column if you spelled the word incorrectly online.

	Word	✓	✗
1	blindfold		X

4. Repeat Steps 1–3 for the remaining words in the Spelling Pretest.

Author Study (A)

Spelling List 1 Pretest

Write each spelling word in the Word column, making sure to spell it correctly.

	Word	✓	✗
1			
2			
3			
4			
5			
6			
7			
8			
9			
10			
11			
12			
13			

	Word	✓	✗
14			
15			
16			
17			
18			
19			
20			
21			
22			
23			
24			
25			

TRY IT
Author Study (A)

Write About Point of View and Theme

Read the passage from from *Sarah, Plain and Tall* by Patricia MacLachlan. Then answer the questions in complete sentences.

> Caleb read and read the letter so many times that the ink began to run and the folds tore. He read the book about sea birds over and over.
>
> "Do you think she'll come?" asked Caleb. "And will she stay? What if she thinks we are loud and pesky?"
>
> "You are loud and pesky," I told him. But I was worried, too. Sarah loved the sea, I could tell. Maybe she wouldn't leave there after all to come where there were fields and grass and sky and not much else.
>
> "What if she comes and doesn't like our house?" Caleb asked. "I told her it was small. Maybe I shouldn't have told her it was small."
>
> "Hush, Caleb. Hush."

1. In *Sarah, Plain and Tall*, Anna is the story's first-person narrator. The narrator's point of view influences our understanding of the story's characters and events.

   a. Based on the passage, what is one thing readers only know because Anna is a first-person narrator? Identify the specific sentence in the passage that reveals it.

   _____
   _____
   _____
   _____
   _____

   b. Name at least one thing that readers do not know because Anna is a first-person narrator.

   _____
   _____
   _____
   _____
   _____
   _____

2. A theme is a big idea that a writer conveys.

   a. What is one of the themes in the first three chapters of *Sarah, Plain and Tall*?

   _____
   _____
   _____

   b. What evidence from the text led you to notice this theme?

   _____
   _____
   _____

GET READY

Author Study (B)

Spelling List 1 Activity Bank

Circle any words in the box that you did not spell correctly on the pretest. Using your circled words, complete one activity of your choice. Complete as much of the activity as you can in the time given.

If you spelled all words correctly on the pretest, complete your chosen activity with as many spelling words as you can.

area	nucleus	ruin	grace	unicorn
diagonal	patio	stereo	gracious	unicycle
diary	pioneer	triumph	graceful	universal
duet	poetry	variety	disgraceful	universe
fluency	rodeo	coyote	symbol	cemetery

Spelling Activity Choices

Vowel-Free Words

1. In the left column, write only the consonants in each word and put a dot where each vowel should be.

2. Spell each word out loud, stating which vowels should be in the places you wrote dots.

3. In the right column, rewrite the entire spelling word.

4. Correct any spelling errors.

Alphabetizing

1. In the left column, write your words from the spelling word list in alphabetical order.

2. Correct any spelling errors.

Parts of Speech

1. In the left column, write the words from your spelling list that are nouns.

2. In the right column, write all the other words from your spelling list and label each word's part of speech.

3. Correct any spelling errors.

Uppercase and Lowercase

1. In the left column, write each of your words in all capital letters, or all uppercase.

2. In the right column, write each of your words in all lowercase letters.

3. Correct any spelling errors.

● **Complete the activity that you chose.**

My chosen activity: _____

1. _____   _____
2. _____   _____
3. _____   _____
4. _____   _____
5. _____   _____
6. _____   _____
7. _____   _____
8. _____   _____
9. _____   _____
10. _____   _____
11. _____   _____
12. _____   _____
13. _____   _____
14. _____   _____
15. _____   _____
16. _____   _____
17. _____   _____
18. _____   _____
19. _____   _____
20. _____   _____
21. _____   _____
22. _____   _____
23. _____   _____
24. _____   _____
25. _____   _____

TRY IT
Author Study (B)

Write a "What If?"

Answer the questions in complete sentences.

1. In Chapter 5 of *Sarah, Plain and Tall*, Sarah tells the Wittings about sliding down the dunes in Maine with her brother. This leads Papa to show Sarah and the children that they have a "dune" of their own: the hay mound that they can climb up and slide down.

    a. What happens when Sarah, Anna, and Caleb slide down the dune?

    _____
    _____
    _____
    _____

    b. Imagine that Papa had never shown them the hay mound or described it as a dune. How might that have changed the story and its themes?

    _____
    _____
    _____
    _____
    _____

2. In Chapter 6 of *Sarah, Plain and Tall*, Sarah and the children talk about winter on the prairie.

   a. Imagine that the characters acted differently in this part of the story. Describe a different version of their conversation about winter. Describe different actions they might have done after their conversation.

   _____
   _____
   _____
   _____
   _____
   _____
   _____
   _____
   _____
   _____
   _____
   _____

   b. What theme does your version of the story convey? Explain.

   _____
   _____
   _____
   _____
   _____
   _____

TRY IT
Author Study (C)

Write a Summary of *Sarah, Plain and Tall*

Write your response in complete sentences.

Write a one-page summary of *Sarah, Plain and Tall*. Be sure to only include each chapter's major events and characters, key details, and important ideas or themes. Remember that your summary should describe events in the same order they happen in the story, and your summary should mention who the narrator of the story is.

_____
_____
_____
_____
_____
_____
_____
_____
_____
_____
_____
_____
_____
_____
_____

In summary, today's weather is quite summery.

TRY IT
Author Study (D)

Compare and Contrast a Character

Write your response in complete sentences.

Choose either Jacob (Papa) or Sarah and write 1 to 2 paragraphs about him or her.

- Describe one way the character has stayed the same from *Sarah, Plain and Tall* to *Caleb's Story*. Use textual details from the books to support your points.

- Describe one way the character has changed from *Sarah, Plain and Tall* to *Caleb's Story*. Use textual details from the books to support your points.

_____
_____
_____
_____
_____
_____
_____
_____
_____
_____
_____
_____

TRY IT
Author Study (E)

Compare and Contrast Settings and Events in Two Stories

Write your response in complete sentences.

Write two paragraphs that compare and contrast the settings and events of *Sarah, Plain and Tall* with those of *Caleb's Story*.

- Paragraph 1: Describe how the time and place in which the stories are set are similar and different.

- Paragraph 2: Explain how the events of the two stories are alike and how they are unique.

Be sure to include details from both stories to support your points.

AUTHOR STUDY (E)

TRY IT
Author Study Wrap-Up

Write About Texts by Patricia MacLachlan

Write your response in complete sentences.

1. Think about the narrator of *Sarah, Plain and Tall* and the narrator of *Caleb's Story*.

    a. Compare and contrast the narrators' points of view. Write about the similarities and differences between the narrators. Remember to use details from the text to support your points.

b. Explain how the narrator's point of view in each story affects the reader's understanding of characters and events.

_____
_____
_____
_____
_____
_____
_____
_____
_____

2. You have read the first four chapters of *Caleb's Story*. There are seven chapters remaining.

   a. Based on what you have read so far, both in *Caleb's Story* and in *Sarah, Plain and Tall*, predict what will happen in the rest of *Caleb's Story*.

   _____
   _____
   _____
   _____
   _____
   _____
   _____
   _____

b. Explain the reason for your prediction, citing details from the text as support.

_____
_____
_____
_____
_____
_____
_____
_____
_____
_____

c. State whether or not you would like to read the rest of *Caleb's Story* and your reasons for feeling as you do.

_____
_____
_____
_____
_____
_____
_____
_____

TRY IT

Context Clues and Word Relationships

Apply: Context Clues and Word Relationships

Use a dictionary or thesaurus to find and list synonyms or antonyms for each vocabulary word.

1. **analyze**
   synonyms: _____

2. **categorize**
   synonyms: _____

3. **structure**
   synonyms: _____

4. **explicit**
   antonyms: _____

Rewrite the sentence or add a second sentence to include a context clue for each vocabulary word's meaning. Use the synonyms and antonyms you listed above to help create each context clue. The first one has been done for you.

5. I got a problem on my math homework wrong, so I had to analyze it.

   New sentence:

   I got a problem on my math homework wrong, so I had to analyze it. I had to study each step to find my error.

CONTEXT CLUES AND WORD RELATIONSHIPS

6. I like to **categorize** my books.

   New sentence:

   _____

   _____

7. The directions for completing the application form were not very **explicit**.

   New sentence:

   _____

   _____

GET READY
Narrative Writing Skills (A)

Spelling List 2 Pretest

1. Open the Spelling Pretest activity online. Listen to the first spelling word. Type the word. Check your answer.

2. Write the correct spelling of the word in the Word column of the Spelling Pretest table on the next page.

	Word	✓	✗
1	blindfold		

3. Put a check mark in the ✓ column if you spelled the word correctly online.

	Word	✓	✗
1	blindfold	✓	

Put an X in the ✗ column if you spelled the word incorrectly online.

	Word	✓	✗
1	blindfold		X

4. Repeat Steps 1–3 for the remaining words in the Spelling Pretest.

Narrative Writing Skills (A)

Spelling List 2 Pretest

Write each spelling word in the Word column, making sure to spell it correctly.

#	Word	✓	✗
1			
2			
3			
4			
5			
6			
7			
8			
9			

#	Word	✓	✗
10			
11			
12			
13			
14			
15			
16			
17			

TRY IT

Narrative Writing Skills (A)

Write What Happens Next

Use the story prompt to answer the questions.

Story prompt: You open the door and find a sealed envelope. What happens next?

1. Think about your story.

   a. Who will narrate the story?

   _____

   b. What other characters will be in the story? Describe at least one character.

   _____

   _____

   c. Where is your story set? Describe the door in more detail.

   _____

   _____

2. Write an introduction to your story that introduces the narrator and the setting. If you choose, introduce other characters. Use your answers to Question 1 to help.

   _____

   _____

   _____

   _____

3. What happens next? Complete the diagram to describe how your story will be organized. (Do not write the whole story now. Just briefly describe what will happen.)

Beginning

↓

Middle

↓

End

GET READY
Narrative Writing Skills (B)

Spelling List 2 Activity Bank

Circle any words in the box that you did not spell correctly on the pretest. Using your circled words, complete one activity of your choice. Complete as much of the activity as you can in the time given.

If you spelled all words correctly on the pretest, complete your chosen activity with as many spelling words as you can.

anchor	schedule	orchestra	microphone	scholar
chemical	chrome	scheme	phantom	scholarship
architect	headache	atmosphere	symphony	scholastic
chord	monarch			

Spelling Activity Choices

Silly Sentences

1. Write a silly sentence using your words from the spelling word list.
2. Underline the spelling word in each sentence.
   Example: The dog was driving a car.
3. Correct any spelling errors.

Spelling Story

1. Write a very short story using your words from the spelling word list.

2. Underline the spelling words in the story.

3. Correct any spelling errors.

Riddle Me This

1. Write a riddle for your words from the spelling word list.
   Example: "I have a trunk, but it's not on my car."

2. Write the answer, which is your word, for each riddle.
   Example: Answer: elephant

3. Correct any spelling errors.

RunOnWord

1. Gather some crayons, colored pencils, or markers. Write each of your words, using a different color for each word, end to end as one long word.
   Example: dogcatbirdfishturtle

2. Rewrite the words correctly and with proper spacing.

- **Complete the activity that you chose.**

    My chosen activity: _____

TRY IT

Narrative Writing Skills (B)

Write About Characters and Events

Use the story prompt to answer the questions.

Story prompt: You open the door and find a sealed envelope. What happens next?

1. Write a sentence that shows a character (or the narrator: you!) performing an action in your story. Do not use the verb *to be* in this sentence.

   _____
   _____

   a. What does this sentence reveal about the character?

   _____
   _____
   _____

   b. What does the sentence reveal about what is happening?

   _____
   _____
   _____

NARRATIVE WRITING SKILLS (B)

2. Imagine the characters in your story. What would they say to each other in the story? In the speech bubbles, write dialogue between two characters. One of those characters can be the narrator.

Character's name _____

Character's name _____

a. What does the dialogue reveal about the characters?

_____
_____

b. What does the dialogue reveal about what is happening?

_____
_____

3. Think about an exciting moment in your story. Maybe it's the moment the narrator solves, or discovers, a mystery related to the letter.

   a. Write about that moment using a slow pace. Really stretch out the moment with many pauses and lots of detail.

   _____
   _____
   _____
   _____

   b. Write about that same moment using a faster pace. Use fewer pauses and less detail.

   _____
   _____
   _____
   _____

4. Write the middle of your story. Use your answers to Questions 1–3 to help.

   _____
   _____
   _____
   _____
   _____
   _____
   _____
   _____
   _____

NARRATIVE WRITING SKILLS (B)

TRY IT
Narrative Writing Skills (C)

Write a Conclusion and Revise Your Word Choice

Use the story prompt to answer the questions.

Story prompt: You open the door and find a sealed envelope. What happens next?

1. Choose a sentence from your response to the prompt. Rewrite the sentence to make it more concrete.

   a. Original sentence:
   _____

   b. Revised sentence:
   _____

2. Choose a sentence from your response to the prompt. Rewrite the sentence so that it includes a transition.

   a. Original sentence:
   _____

   b. Revised sentence:
   _____

3. Write the conclusion to your story.

_____
_____
_____
_____
_____
_____
_____
_____
_____
_____
_____
_____

May I *please* read your story?

TRY IT
Narrative Writing Skills Wrap-Up

Use Narrative Writing Skills

Choose a prompt from the list, or write your own prompt.

Story prompts:

- You are having dinner with your favorite athlete. What happens?
- You travel back in time to when your grandparents were children. What happens?
- You suddenly have the ability to talk to animals. What happens?

Use your prompt to answer the questions.

1. Who will narrate your story?
   _____
   _____

2. Where will the setting of your story be? Be more specific than the prompt. For example, write *where* and *when* your story takes place.
   _____
   _____
   _____

3. Write a short introduction. Use description to give information about your narrator and setting. You can use dialogue, if you choose. Remember, *show*, don't tell.

_____
_____
_____
_____

4. Briefly describe what would happen in the middle of your story.

_____
_____
_____

5. Write a sentence (or sentences) that could be in your story. In these sentences, use sensory detail to show what's happening.

_____
_____
_____
_____

6. Write dialogue that could be in your story.

Character's name　　　　　　　　**Character's name**

_____　　　　　　　_____

a. What is one detail this dialogue reveals about the characters?

_____
_____

b. What is one detail this dialogue reveals about what is happening?

_____
_____

NARRATIVE WRITING SKILLS WRAP-UP

7. Briefly describe what would happen in the conclusion to your story. Explain how your conclusion makes sense with the rest of your story.

_____
_____
_____
_____
_____
_____

8. Which part of your story would have a slow pace? Explain.

_____
_____
_____
_____
_____

GET READY

The Mary Celeste (A)

Spelling List 3 Pretest

1. Open the Spelling Pretest activity online. Listen to the first spelling word. Type the word. Check your answer.

2. Write the correct spelling of the word in the Word column of the Spelling Pretest table on the next page.

	Word	✓	✗
1	blindfold		

3. Put a check mark in the ✓ column if you spelled the word correctly online.

	Word	✓	✗
1	blindfold	✓	

Put an X in the ✗ column if you spelled the word incorrectly online.

	Word	✓	✗
1	blindfold		X

4. Repeat Steps 1–3 for the remaining words in the Spelling Pretest.

The Mary Celeste (A)

Spelling List 3 Pretest

Write each spelling word in the Word column, making sure to spell it correctly.

Word	✓	✗
1		
2		
3		
4		
5		
6		
7		
8		
9		

Word	✓	✗
10		
11		
12		
13		
14		
15		
16		
17		

TRY IT

The Mary Celeste (A)

Write About the Main Idea and Make Predictions

Write your responses in complete sentences.

1. Consider what you have read in *The Mary Celeste: An Unsolved Mystery from History* so far. What is the overall main idea of this first section of the book? Which supporting details led you to this main idea?

2. You have read up to the point where three crew members of the *Dei Gratia* are rowing over to the *Mary Celeste* in a small boat. What do you think they will find? Make a prediction about the upcoming reading. Be sure to base your prediction on the details in the reading you have already completed. Describe those details to support your prediction.

_____
_____
_____
_____
_____
_____
_____
_____
_____
_____
_____
_____
_____

GET READY

The Mary Celeste (B)

Spelling List 3 Activity Bank

Circle any words in the box that you did not spell correctly on the pretest. Using your circled words, complete one activity of your choice. Complete as much of the activity as you can in the time given.

If you spelled all words correctly on the pretest, complete your chosen activity with as many spelling words as you can.

ability	amend	fauna	pizza	deficiency
adobe	aware	flora	plasma	deficient
algebra	data	pasta	scuba	deficit
allowance	drama			

Spelling Activity Choices

Hidden Words

1. Draw a picture and "hide" as many words from the Spelling Word List inside the picture as you can.
2. See if others can find the words within the picture.

Triangle Spelling

Write each word in a triangle.

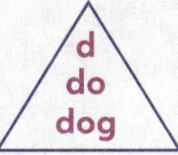

Ghost Words

1. Use a white crayon to write each spelling word.
2. Go over the white crayon writing with a colored marker.

THE MARY CELESTE (B) 47

Complete the activity that you chose.

My chosen activity: _____

48   THE MARY CELESTE (B)

TRY IT
The Mary Celeste (B)

Write About the Ship's Log

Write your responses in complete sentences.

In this section of *The Mary Celeste: An Unsolved Mystery from History*, Jane Yolen states that the men exploring the *Mary Celeste* found the ship's log. She notes that the last entry was on November 25—about 10 days before the *Dei Gratia* found the ship—and that no trouble was noted in the log. Imagine that there was one more entry in the log. What are three key details that might have explained what happened on the *Mary Celeste*? What are two minor details that might not have been helpful in understanding what happened to the crew?

Ahoy, mate. I wonder if we wrote the same clues. Gray clouds swirled . . . .

TRY IT

The Mary Celeste (C)

Write a Summary

Write your responses in complete sentences.

Write a summary of the last section of *The Mary Celeste: An Unsolved Mystery from History*. In your summary, be sure to state the main ideas from this part of the book and several key details. Your summary should be mostly paraphrased. You should retell events in your own words, but it is acceptable to include one direct quotation from the text. If you include a direct quotation, remember to quote accurately and use quotation marks.

TRY IT

The Mary Celeste Wrap-Up

Write About *The Mary Celeste*

Write your response in complete sentences.

The final pages of *The Mary Celeste: An Unsolved Mystery from History* offer several theories about what happened to the people on board the ship, and the narrator says she has her own theory.

- Based on what you read in the book, what do you think took place? Why have you taken this position?
- Describe your theory about the events that led to the abandonment of the *Mary Celeste* and provide several details from the text that support it.
- Be sure to also include at least one direct quotation that helps support your theory.

_____
_____
_____
_____
_____
_____
_____
_____
_____
_____
_____
_____
_____

54 THE MARY CELESTE WRAP-UP

GET READY

Narrative Writing: Prewriting (A)

Spelling List 4 Pretest

1. Open the Spelling Pretest activity online. Listen to the first spelling word. Type the word. Check your answer.

2. Write the correct spelling of the word in the Word column of the Spelling Pretest table on the next page.

	Word	✓	✗
1	blindfold		

3. Put a check mark in the ✓ column if you spelled the word correctly online.

	Word	✓	✗
1	blindfold	✓	

Put an X in the ✗ column if you spelled the word incorrectly online.

	Word	✓	✗
1	blindfold		X

4. Repeat Steps 1–3 for the remaining words in the Spelling Pretest.

Narrative Writing: Prewriting (A)

Spelling List 4 Pretest

Write each spelling word in the Word column, making sure to spell it correctly.

#	Word	✓	✗
1			
2			
3			
4			
5			
6			
7			
8			
9			

#	Word	✓	✗
10			
11			
12			
13			
14			
15			
16			
17			

TRY IT

Narrative Writing: Prewriting (A)

Brainstorm for Your Personal Narrative

Read the writing assignment. You will complete the assignment in steps over multiple lessons.

Prompt: Write about a meaningful moment in your life.

Requirements: Your narrative should have

- A **title**

- A logical sequence, including an **introduction**, **body**, and **conclusion**

- A well-developed **narrator** and at least one other **character**, as well as a clear **setting**

- **Dialogue** and **description** that develop events and show how characters respond to situations

- Appropriate **pacing**

- **Sensory language** and **transitions**

- Correct **grammar**, **usage**, and **mechanics**

Audience: Your teacher and peers

Purpose: Show readers why the experience was meaningful.

Length: 500–700 words long; approximately 8 handwritten drafting pages or 2 pages typed and double-spaced

Brainstorm and choose a topic for your personal narrative.

1. List as many possible topics as you can think of.

   _____   _____
   _____   _____
   _____   _____
   _____   _____
   _____   _____

2. Read your list of topics. Circle any topics that you really would like to write about. If you didn't circle any topics, add a few more to your list.

3. Choose your favorite topic that you circled. Then answer Yes or No to each question.

   a. Is the topic small enough to describe in detail in just a few pages? _____

   b. Is the topic something you can *show* with description, dialogue, and sensory words? _____

   c. Is the topic meaningful to you? _____

4. Did you answer Yes to Parts A–C of Question 3? You have found a topic! If not, go back and complete Question 3 with another topic from your list. Repeat until you find a topic that works.

My personal narrative topic is

_____

GET READY

Narrative Writing: Prewriting (B)

Spelling List 4 Activity Bank

Circle any words or abbreviations in the box that you did not spell correctly on the pretest. Using your circled words, complete one activity of your choice. Complete as much of the activity as you can in the time given.

If you spelled all words correctly on the pretest, complete your chosen activity with as many spelling words as you can.

lb	pound	sq	vol.	amateur
ounce	pt	square	volume	colonel
oz	qt	versus	vs.	maneuver
pint	quart			

Spelling Activity Choices

Create a Crossword

1. Write a word from your spelling word list in the center of the grid paper.

2. Write another spelling word going across and sharing a letter with the first word. See how many words you can connect.

    Example:

			p			
		k	i	s	s	e	s
	d		n			
r	o	c	k	s		
	g					
	s					

Word Search Puzzle

1. Draw a box on the grid paper. The box should be large enough to hold your words from the spelling word list.

2. Fill in the grid paper with words from your spelling list, writing them horizontally, vertically, and diagonally (forwards or backwards if you choose).

3. Fill in the rest of the box with random letters.

4. Ask someone to find and circle your spelling words in the puzzle you made.

- **Complete the activity that you chose.**

  My chosen activity: _____

NARRATIVE WRITING: PREWRITING (B)

TRY IT

Narrative Writing: Prewriting (B)

Prewrite for Your Personal Narrative

Answer the questions to plan your personal narrative.

1. Describe the beginning, middle, and end of your narrative.

My Topic _____

Beginning

Middle

End

2. List details about your setting (you don't need to write complete sentences). Use concrete and sensory language. Include at least three of the five senses. If you wish, you can draw a picture to help you plan.

3. List three feelings the narrator has during the events in your narrative. Write either a short description or a short dialogue that shows each feeling.

Feeling	Description or Dialogue

NARRATIVE WRITING: PREWRITING (B)

TRY IT

Narrative Writing: Drafting (A)

Draft Your Personal Narrative

Write the first draft of your personal narrative. Write only on the white rows. You will use the purple rows for revisions later.

Title _____

start here ▶

keep writing ▶

Draft Page 1

keep writing ▶

Draft Page 2

keep writing ▶

Draft Page 3

Draft Page 4

keep writing ▶

Draft Page 5

keep writing ▶

Draft Page 7

NARRATIVE WRITING: DRAFTING (A)

TRY IT

Nuance

Apply: Nuance

For each sentence, choose the word that best completes the sentence and explain your choice. Think about the nuances, or small differences in meaning, between the two choices.

1. I wrote a card to express my _____ to our neighbor after her dog died.

   Would you choose *sympathy* or *sensitivity* to complete this sentence? Why?

   _____
   _____

2. My friend Lou always showed _____ and listened when I wanted to talk about something I was having trouble with or a challenge I was facing.

   Would you choose *sympathy* or *compassion* to complete this sentence? Why?

   _____
   _____

3. The downpour lasted longer than expected, and after several hours a _____ of rain was streaming down every street and began to flood some of the parked cars.

   Would you choose *influx* or *torrent* to complete this sentence? Why?

   _____
   _____

NUANCE

4. He turned on the water to fill the bathtub and left to get a towel, but by the time he returned, a soapy _____ from the tub was steadily pouring onto the floor.

Would you choose *torrent* or *overflow* to complete this sentence? Why?

_____

_____

5. If you like to read mysteries that take up all of your attention, I highly recommend this one because it will _____ you, and you will not want to stop reading.

Would you choose *devour* or *engross* to complete this sentence? Why?

_____

_____

6. Because I missed lunch this afternoon, I am certain that I am going to _____ every single morsel of food on my plate at dinner and will probably want to eat more!

Would you choose *consume* or *devour* to complete this sentence? Why?

_____

_____

Answer the questions.

7. Write your own sentence using the word *sympathy*, *compassion*, or *sensitivity*, leaving a blank space where your chosen word belongs. Have someone else read your sentence. Ask this person to choose whether *sympathy*, *compassion*, or *sensitivity* best completes the sentence. Discuss his or her answer.

_____

_____

8. Write your own sentence using the word *influx*, *torrent*, or *overflow*, leaving a blank space where your chosen word belongs. Have someone else read your sentence. Ask this person to choose whether *influx*, *torrent*, or *overflow* best completes the sentence. Discuss his or her answer.

_____

_____

9. Write your own sentence using the word *devour*, *consume*, or *engross*, leaving a blank space where your chosen word belongs. Have someone else read your sentence. Ask this person to choose whether *devour*, *consume*, or *engross* best completes the sentence. Discuss his or her answer.

_____

_____

GET READY

Mesmerized (A)

Spelling List 5 Pretest

1. Open the Spelling Pretest activity online. Listen to the first spelling word. Type the word. Check your answer.

2. Write the correct spelling of the word in the Word column of the Spelling Pretest table on the next page.

	Word	✓	✗
1	blindfold		

3. Put a check mark in the ✓ column if you spelled the word correctly online.

	Word	✓	✗
1	blindfold	✓	

Put an X in the ✗ column if you spelled the word incorrectly online.

	Word	✓	✗
1	blindfold		X

4. Repeat Steps 1–3 for the remaining words in the Spelling Pretest.

Mesmerized (A)

Spelling List 5 Pretest

Write each spelling word in the Word column, making sure to spell it correctly.

#	Word	✓	✗
1			
2			
3			
4			
5			
6			
7			
8			
9			

#	Word	✓	✗
10			
11			
12			
13			
14			
15			
16			
17			

TRY IT

Mesmerized (A)

Write About Franklin and Mesmer

Write your responses in complete sentences.

1. Turn to pages 12 and 13 in *Mesmerized* by Mara Rockliff. Describe the comparisons that Rockliff makes when she describes Franklin and Mesmer. What do the comparisons suggest about each man's personality?

2. The word *mesmerized* means "entranced" or "hypnotized." It comes from Dr. Mesmer's name. Why does the word *mesmerized* mean this? Cite the specific language that Rockliff uses in the text that helps explain the word's meaning.

_____
_____
_____
_____
_____
_____
_____
_____
_____
_____
_____
_____

GET READY

Mesmerized (B)

Spelling List 5 Activity Bank

Circle any words in the box that you did not spell correctly on the pretest. Using your circled words, complete one activity of your choice. Complete as much of the activity as you can in the time given.

If you spelled all words correctly on the pretest, complete your chosen activity with as many spelling words as you can.

comparable	major	preside	resignation	apprehend
compare	majority	president	restoration	comprehend
janitor	perspiration	resign	restore	comprehensive
janitorial	perspire			

Spelling Activity Choices

Vowel-Free Words

1. In the left column, write only the consonants in each word and put a dot where each vowel should be.

2. Spell each word out loud, stating which vowels should be in the places you wrote dots.

3. In the right column, rewrite the entire spelling word.

4. Correct any spelling errors.

Alphabetizing

1. In the left column, write your words from the spelling word list in alphabetical order.

2. Correct any spelling errors.

Parts of Speech

1. In the left column, write the words from your spelling list that are nouns.

2. In the right column, write all the other words from your spelling list and label each word's part of speech.

3. Correct any spelling errors.

Uppercase and Lowercase

1. In the left column, write each of your words in all capital letters, or all uppercase.

2. In the right column, write each of your words in all lowercase letters.

3. Correct any spelling errors.

Complete the activity that you chose.

My chosen activity: _____

1. _____
2. _____
3. _____
4. _____
5. _____
6. _____
7. _____
8. _____
9. _____
10. _____
11. _____
12. _____
13. _____
14. _____
15. _____
16. _____
17. _____
18. _____
19. _____
20. _____
21. _____
22. _____
23. _____
24. _____

TRY IT

Mesmerized (B)

Write About Multiple Main Ideas

Write your response in complete sentences.

Turn to pages 36 and 37 in *Mesmerized* by Mara Rockliff.

- What are two main ideas in this part of the book?
- Identify the details from the text—including the specific language that Rockliff uses—that led you to these main ideas.
- Describe any inferences you made and how they also support these main ideas.

_____
_____

_____
_____
_____
_____

TRY IT

Mesmerized (C)

Summarize *Mesmerized*

Write your response in complete sentences.

Write a one-page summary of *Mesmerized*. Be sure to include the text's key details, major events, important figures, and main ideas. Remember that your summary should describe events in the same order they happen in the text. Also, you may quote from the text, but be sure to do so accurately.

MESMERIZED (C) **87**

TRY IT

Mesmerized Wrap-Up

Write About Ben Franklin

Write your responses in complete sentences.

1. Think about how Mara Rockliff depicts Ben Franklin and the time he spent in Paris in *Mesmerized*.

    a. Describe Ben Franklin. Include details from the text and at least one direct quotation from the text that supports your description.

    _____
    _____
    _____
    _____
    _____
    _____
    _____
    _____
    _____
    _____

b. Explain how the people of France felt about Franklin. Why did they feel as they did? Again, provide details from the text and a direct quotation that supports your explanation.

_____
_____
_____
_____
_____
_____
_____
_____
_____

2. Based on what you read in *Mesmerized*, what can you infer about the way Franklin felt about Paris and the French people when he was there? Which details from the text led you to this inference?

_____
_____
_____
_____
_____
_____
_____
_____
_____
_____

TRY IT

Narrative Writing: Revising

Revise Your Personal Narrative

Use the checklist as you revise your personal narrative draft.

Organization

- ☐ Does my introduction give enough information about the situation, narrator, and main characters?

- ☐ Are any ideas in the wrong place?

- ☐ Do I use clear and logical transitions?

- ☐ Does my conclusion make sense and answer important questions?

Content

- ☐ Do I show how the narrator and characters respond to situations by using dialogue or description?

- ☐ Do I show events by using dialogue or description?

- ☐ Is the pacing of my ideas appropriate?

- ☐ Are there details I can show instead of tell?

- ☐ Are there words or phrases that could be more concrete?

TRY IT

Narrative Writing: Proofreading

Proofread Your Personal Narrative

Use the checklist as you proofread your personal narrative draft.

Grammar and Usage

- [ ] Are all sentences complete and correct?
- [ ] Are there any missing or extra words?
- [ ] Are all verbs in the appropriate tense?
- [ ] Are there any inappropriate shifts in verb tense?
- [ ] Are there any agreement errors?
- [ ] Are there other grammatical or usage errors?

Mechanics

- [ ] Is the title capitalized correctly and enclosed in quotation marks?
- [ ] Is every word spelled correctly, including frequently confused words?
- [ ] Does every sentence begin with a capital letter and end with the appropriate punctuation?
- [ ] Is dialogue punctuated correctly?
- [ ] Are there other punctuation or capitalization errors?

GET READY

Queen of the Falls

Spelling List 6 Pretest

1. Open the Spelling Pretest activity online. Listen to the first spelling word. Type the word. Check your answer.

2. Write the correct spelling of the word in the Word column of the Spelling Pretest table on the next page.

	Word	✓	✗
1	blindfold		

3. Put a check mark in the ✓ column if you spelled the word correctly online.

	Word	✓	✗
1	blindfold	✓	

Put an X in the ✗ column if you spelled the word incorrectly online.

	Word	✓	✗
1	blindfold		X

4. Repeat Steps 1–3 for the remaining words in the Spelling Pretest.

Queen of the Falls

Spelling List 6 Pretest

Write each spelling word in the Word column, making sure to spell it correctly.

#	Word	✓	✗
1			
2			
3			
4			
5			
6			
7			
8			
9			
10			
11			

#	Word	✓	✗
12			
13			
14			
15			
16			
17			
18			
19			
20			
21			

TRY IT

Queen of the Falls

Write About Annie Taylor

Write your responses in complete sentences.

1. What were Annie Taylor's stated reasons for wanting to go over Niagara Falls in a barrel? Include at least one direct quotation from *Queen of the Falls* to support your answer.

2. Annie's stunt was successful, but it did not make her rich. In the years after 1901, she returned to Niagara Falls to sell souvenirs and to tell those who would listen about her life and her death-defying ride. Based on what it says in the text, what can you infer about Annie and how she came to view her stunt during these years? Include at least one direct quotation from *Queen of the Falls* that supports your inference.

GET READY

Queen of the Falls Wrap-Up

Spelling List 6 Activity Bank

Circle any words in the box that you did not spell correctly on the pretest. Using your circled words, complete one activity of your choice. Complete as much of the activity as you can in the time given.

If you spelled all words correctly on the pretest, complete your chosen activity with as many spelling words as you can.

budget	accept	vaccination	dungeon	toxic
gadget	cyclone	gigantic	gauge	detoxify
hedgehog	concept	gorgeous	sergeant	toxin
trudge	scarce	suggest	geyser	
accent	success			

Spelling Activity Choices

Silly Sentences

1. Write a silly sentence using your words from the spelling word list.

2. Underline the spelling word in each sentence.
   Example: The dog was driving a car.

3. Correct any spelling errors.

Spelling Story

1. Write a very short story using your words from the spelling word list.

2. Underline the spelling words in the story.

3. Correct any spelling errors.

Riddle Me This

1. Write a riddle for your words from the spelling word list.
   Example: "I have a trunk, but it's not on my car."

2. Write the answer, which is your word, for each riddle.
   Example: Answer: elephant

3. Correct any spelling errors.

RunOnWord

1. Gather some crayons, colored pencils, or markers. Write each of your words, ussing a different color for each word, end to end as one long word.
   Example: dogcatbirdfishturtle

2. Rewrite the words correctly and with proper spacing.

- **Complete the activity that you chose.**

    My chosen activity: _____

TRY IT

Queen of the Falls Wrap-Up

Write About *Queen of the Falls*

Write your response in complete sentences.

Write a one-page summary of *Queen of the Falls*. Be sure to include its key details, major events, important figures, and main ideas. Remember that your summary should describe events in the same order they happen in the text. Also, you may quote from the text, but be sure to do so accurately.

QUEEN OF THE FALLS WRAP-UP 103

TRY IT
Where Is Niagara Falls? (A)

Write About the Main Ideas of Chapters 3 and 4

Write your responses in complete sentences.

1. Review Chapter 3 of *Where Is Niagara Falls?* by Megan Stine.
   - What is one main idea of this chapter?
   - Identify at least two key details from the text—including the specific language that Stine uses—that led you to this main idea.

WHERE IS NIAGARA FALLS? (A)

2. Review Chapter 4 of *Where Is Niagara Falls?* by Megan Stine.

    - What is one main idea of this chapter?
    - Identify at least two key details from the text—including the specific language that Stine uses—that led you to this main idea.

TRY IT

Where Is Niagara Falls? (B)

Write About Viewpoints and Write a Summary

Write your responses in complete sentences.

1. Reread page 64 of *Where Is Niagara Falls?* Then answer these questions:
   - What is Megan Stine's view of William A. Banks? Why?
   - How does Stine's view of Banks compare to Chris Van Allsburg's view of Annie Taylor's second manager?
   - How did the behavior of Frank Russell and William A. (Billy) Banks affect Annie Taylor?

2. Write a one-page summary of *Where Is Niagara Falls?* Be sure to include the text's key details, major events, important figures, and main ideas. Remember that your summary should describe events in the same order they happen in the text. Also, you may quote from the text, but be sure to do so accurately.

In 50,000 years, Niagara Falls may be gone because of erosion.

TRY IT

Where Is Niagara Falls? Wrap-Up

Write About *Where Is Niagara Falls?*

Write your response in the spaces provided.

When you must write an informational essay about a topic, an important early step in the process is creating an outline. Outlines can help you organize the information you find when reading or doing research.

Imagine that you had to write an informational essay on Niagara Falls. Complete the outline below with information you found in *Where Is Niagara Falls?* by Megan Stine.

Because this is only an outline, you do not have to write in complete sentences. However, be sure that what you include are key details, major events, important figures, and main ideas from the reading. Leave out minor details, less important events and figures, and ideas that are not central to the topic.

Niagara Falls

I. **Formation**

    a. When: _____

    _____

    b. How: _____

    _____

    _____

    c. Location _____

    _____

    _____

II. **Human Encounters**

   a. Before Europeans came to North America: _____
   _____

   b. After Europeans came to North America: _____
   _____
   _____

   c. People's reactions: _____
   _____
   _____

III. **Importance/Role in Modern Times**

   a. Major nineteenth-century events or developments: _____
   _____
   _____
   _____

   b. Major twentieth-century events or developments: _____
   _____
   _____

   c. Niagara Falls today: _____
   _____
   _____
   _____

TRY IT

Dictionary Skills

Apply: More Dictionary Skills Practice

Using a dictionary, look up and review the dictionary entry for each vocabulary word in the box. Then answer the questions.

abhor	impulse	muster
naught	renown	thrifty
vacancy		

1. Which words are verbs?

   _____

2. Which words are pronounced by placing the stress on the second syllable?

   _____

3. Which word rhymes with *thought*?

   _____

4. Which word has three syllables?

   _____

5. What is the meaning of *vacancy*?

   _____

6. Synonyms are words whose meanings are the same or nearly the same. What is one synonym for *impulse*?

   _____

7. We need to set out all the chairs and tables for the community potluck supper now. I will _____ all the members of our group to do this job together.

   Based on context clues and the definitions in the dictionary entries, which word correctly completes the sentence? Why?

   _____

   _____

8. I learned to be careful with money by shopping with my mom. She was _____ , trying not to spend too much on any item in the market. She said it was the way to save up extra money for later on.

   Based on context clues and the definitions in the dictionary entries, which word correctly completes the sentence? Why?

   _____

   _____

9. When my aunt moved out of our house, we had an empty room to rent out. Martin came to view the room when he saw our ad about the _____ . My mother agreed to rent the room to him for a year, and he moved in the next day.

   Based on context clues and the definitions in the dictionary entries, which word correctly completes the sentence? Why?

   _____

   _____

Rewrite the sentence or add a second sentence to give a context clue for the meaning of each vocabulary word. The first one has been done for you.

10. I *abhor* having mushrooms on my pizza.

    New sentence:

    I abhor having mushrooms on my pizza. They really disgust me.

11. Jaime had an *impulse* to run out into the rain.

    _____
    _____

12. The novels of Charles Dickens have achieved great *renown*.

    _____
    _____

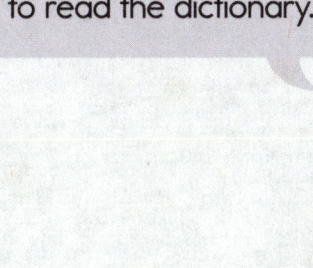

I have a strange impulse to read the dictionary.

TRY IT

Government Words

Apply: Government Words

Read the paragraph. Think about any context clues, antonyms, or synonyms and what they suggest about the missing word.

1. My grandfather was always very interested in government, so he decided on a career in _____ service. He began as a researcher for the federal government. He helped create policies that improved the working conditions for his fellow citizens. Later, he worked for the agency that sets the guidelines for food safety.

   a. Which word correctly fills in the blank? *civil* or *democracy*

   b. Explanation:

   _____

   _____

2. Rita became a lawyer because she wanted to fight the unfairness she saw in society. Each day, she worked to help those who were not treated equally. She tried to make sure that they always received _____ in court.

   a. Which word correctly fills in the blank? *liberty* or *justice*

   b. Explanation:

   _____

   _____

GOVERNMENT WORDS **117**

3. Religious freedom has deep roots in Maryland. In the 1600s, the colonial government passed an act that protected the rights of people to worship as they pleased. This decision to _____ many different religious views and allow people to attend whatever church they wanted to attend was extremely important. It was one of the ways in which the American colonies were different from many countries in Europe at the time.

   a. Which word correctly fills in the blank? *emancipate* or *tolerate*

   b. Explanation:

   _____

   _____

4. People have power in a _____ , but they also have responsibilities. They must make decisions about how their government will work and what laws it will have. One way that people exercise their power in this form of government is by voting.

   a. Which word correctly fills in the blank? *democracy* or *constitution*

   b. Explanation:

   _____

   _____

118 GOVERNMENT WORDS

- Write a sentence using the given government word.
  - Have someone else read your sentence.
  - Explain to this person how the meaning of the given government word can be understood based on context clues, synonyms, antonyms, or reasoning.

5. *constitution*

   Sentence:

   _____
   _____

6. *liberty*

   Sentence:

   _____
   _____

7. *emancipate*

   Sentence:

   _____
   _____

GET READY
A Wrinkle in Time (A)

Spelling List 7 Pretest

1. Open the Spelling Pretest activity online. Listen to the first spelling word. Type the word. Check your answer.

2. Write the correct spelling of the word in the Word column of the Spelling Pretest table on the next page.

	Word	✓	✗
1	blindfold		

3. Put a check mark in the ✓ column if you spelled the word correctly online.

	Word	✓	✗
1	blindfold	✓	

Put an X in the ✗ column if you spelled the word incorrectly online.

	Word	✓	✗
1	blindfold		X

4. Repeat Steps 1–3 for the remaining words in the Spelling Pretest.

A Wrinkle in Time (A)

Spelling List 7 Pretest

Write each spelling word in the Word column, making sure to spell it correctly.

	Word	✓	✗
1			
2			
3			
4			
5			
6			
7			
8			
9			

	Word	✓	✗
10			
11			
12			
13			
14			
15			
16			
17			

TRY IT

A Wrinkle in Time (A)

Write About Chapter 1 and Visualize the Text

Answer the question in complete sentences.

1. Chapter 1 ends with Mrs. Whatsit saying a word—*tesseract*—that stuns Mrs. Murry. This leaves the Murrys and readers eager to know more about Mrs. Whatsit and the role she will play. What do you think will happen next? Make a prediction about the upcoming chapters.

    _____
    _____

2. Active readers use visualizing as an important strategy to bring texts to life. Choose a character or moment from the first chapter of the novel and draw how you imagine that person or event.

GET READY

A Wrinkle in Time (B)

Spelling List 7 Activity Bank

Circle any words in the box that you did not spell correctly on the pretest. Using your circled words, complete one activity of your choice. Complete as much of the activity as you can in the time given.

If you spelled all words correctly on the pretest, complete your chosen activity with as many spelling words as you can.

advantage	atom	physical	sentiment	coupon
advantageous	atomic	physician	rhyme	souvenir
angel	bomb	sense	rhythm	tournament
angelic	bombard			

Spelling Activity Choices

Hidden Words

1. Draw a picture and "hide" as many words from the Spelling Word List inside the picture as you can.
2. See if others can find the words within the picture.

Triangle Spelling

Write each word in a triangle.

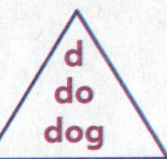

Ghost Words

1. Use a white crayon to write each spelling word.
2. Go over the white crayon writing with a colored marker.

A WRINKLE IN TIME (B)

Complete the activity that you chose.

My chosen activity: _____

TRY IT
A Wrinkle in Time (B)

Write a Summary of Chapters 1–3

Write your response in complete sentences.

In 1–2 paragraphs, summarize the first three chapters of *A Wrinkle in Time*. In your summary, use at least one direct quotation from the text that supports an important idea or point or that helps reveal something about a character.

TRY IT
A Wrinkle in Time (C)

Write About the Text

Write your response in complete sentences.

Imagine *A Wrinkle in Time* as a somewhat different book. Instead of having a third-person narrator who focuses on Meg, imagine the novel with a third-person narrator who focuses on Mrs. Whatsit. How would your understanding of the characters and events of the book change if the book's narrator focused on Mrs. Whatsit instead of Meg?

TRY IT
A Wrinkle in Time (D)

Write About Characters

Write your responses in complete sentences.

In 1–2 paragraphs, compare and contrast two characters from *A Wrinkle in Time*. Be sure to describe how they are alike and how they are different, and use at least one direct quotation from the text to support your points.

GET READY

A Wrinkle in Time (E)

Spelling List 8 Pretest

1. Open the Spelling Pretest activity online. Listen to the first spelling word. Type the word. Check your answer.

2. Write the correct spelling of the word in the Word column of the Spelling Pretest table on the next page.

	Word	✓	✗
1	blindfold		

3. Put a check mark in the ✓ column if you spelled the word correctly online.

	Word	✓	✗
1	blindfold	✓	

Put an X in the ✗ column if you spelled the word incorrectly online.

	Word	✓	✗
1	blindfold		X

4. Repeat Steps 1–3 for the remaining words in the Spelling Pretest.

A Wrinkle in Time (E)

Spelling List 8 Pretest

Write each spelling word in the Word column, making sure to spell it correctly.

#	Word	✓	✗
1			
2			
3			
4			
5			
6			
7			
8			
9			
10			
11			
12			
13			

#	Word	✓	✗
14			
15			
16			
17			
18			
19			
20			
21			
22			
23			
24			
25			

TRY IT
A Wrinkle in Time (E)

Write About Challenges and Themes

Write your response in complete sentences.

In Chapter 6 of *A Wrinkle in Time*, the children travel to the planet Camazotz. There, they are left by themselves and told to go into the town. When they do so, the town they enter is familiar in some ways and quite strange in others. What challenge do Meg, Charles Wallace, and Calvin face in the town? How do they respond to this challenge? What theme can you see developing based on their response to their situation?

GET READY

A Wrinkle in Time (F)

Spelling List 8 Activity Bank

Circle any words in the box that you did not spell correctly on the pretest. Using your circled words, complete one activity of your choice. Complete as much of the activity as you can in the time given.

If you spelled all words correctly on the pretest, complete your chosen activity with as many spelling words as you can.

could've	they'd	who'd	diameter	nourish
we're	they'll	who'll	perimeter	multicolored
should've	they've	haven't	speedometer	multinational
that's	weren't	you've	adjourn	multimedia
hasn't	what's	we'll	flourish	multiple

Spelling Activity Choices

Create a Crossword

1. Write a word from your spelling word list in the center of the grid paper.

2. Write another spelling word going across and sharing a letter with the first word. See how many words you can connect.

    Example:

			p			
		k	i	s	s	e	s
	d		n			
r	o	c	k	s		
	g					
	s					

Word Search Puzzle

1. Draw a box on the grid paper. The box should be large enough to hold your words from the spelling word list.

2. Fill in the grid paper with words from your spelling list, writing them horizontally, vertically, and diagonally (forwards or backwards if you choose).

3. Fill in the rest of the box with random letters.

4. Ask someone to find and circle your spelling words in the puzzle you made.

- **Complete the activity that you chose.**

  My chosen activity: _____

TRY IT
A Wrinkle in Time (F)

Write About Charles Wallace

Write your response in complete sentences.

In Chapters 7 and 8 of *A Wrinkle in Time*, the children meet the man with red eyes and confront real danger. Consider what Charles Wallace says and does in these chapters. What can you infer about his character based on his words and his actions? Include specific examples and evidence from the text, as well as direct quotations, to support your response.

TRY IT

A Wrinkle in Time (G)

Write About Two Settings

Write your response in complete sentences.

The first several chapters of *A Wrinkle in Time* take place on Earth, while much of Chapters 7, 8, and 9 take place on Camazotz. In 1–2 paragraphs, compare and contrast Earth and Camazotz. How are the two planets alike? How are they different? Include details from the text, as well as direct quotations, to support your response.

TRY IT

A Wrinkle in Time (H)

Write About Another Theme

Write your response in complete sentences.

Think about what you have read so far in *A Wrinkle in Time*. Think about the problems the characters have faced, how they have reacted, and what they have realized or recognized, based on the events of the story. Then name one theme that the novel has conveyed to this point. Explain how you determined that L'Engle conveys this theme, and include at least one direct quotation from the book that supports it.

TRY IT

A Wrinkle in Time (I)

Write About Chapter 12

Write your responses in complete sentences.

Think about the final chapter of *A Wrinkle in Time*. Consider the most important events and details in the chapter. Then write a 1–2 paragraph summary of the chapter. Remember that your summary should describe events in the same order as Madeleine L'Engle's novel, and be sure to leave out descriptions of minor or unimportant figures and moments.

_____
_____
_____
_____
_____
_____
_____
_____
_____
_____
_____
_____
_____
_____
_____

_____
_____
_____
_____
_____
_____
_____
_____
_____
_____
_____
_____
_____

Who should I include?
Which details?
Whatsit about?

TRY IT

A Wrinkle in Time Wrap-Up

Write About *A Wrinkle in Time*

Write a book review of *A Wrinkle in Time* by Madeleine L'Engle. Write your response in complete sentences.

Follow these guidelines in writing your review:

- Your review should be at least three paragraphs long.
- Describe several of the most important events, characters, and ideas in the novel.
- Include specific examples and direct quotations from the text.
- Explain why others should read the book.

NOTE: Remember that the goal of this review is to encourage others to read the novel, not to explain every moment or event. For example, you don't need to describe the ending of the novel in your review because readers can enjoy discovering that for themselves.

_____
_____
_____
_____
_____
_____
_____
_____

Informational Writing Skills (A)

Spelling List 9 Pretest

1. Open the Spelling Pretest activity online. Listen to the first spelling word. Type the word. Check your answer.

2. Write the correct spelling of the word in the Word column of the Spelling Pretest table on the next page.

	Word	✓	✗
1	blindfold		

3. Put a check mark in the ✓ column if you spelled the word correctly online.

	Word	✓	✗
1	blindfold	✓	

Put an X in the ✗ column if you spelled the word incorrectly online.

	Word	✓	✗
1	blindfold		X

4. Repeat Steps 1–3 for the remaining words in the Spelling Pretest.

Informational Writing Skills (A)

Spelling List 9 Pretest

Write each spelling word in the Word column, making sure to spell it correctly.

	Word	✓	✗
1			
2			
3			
4			
5			
6			
7			
8			
9			

	Word	✓	✗
10			
11			
12			
13			
14			
15			
16			
17			

TRY IT

Informational Writing Skills (A)

Write About a Celestial Body

Use the prompt to answer the questions.

Prompt: Write an informational paragraph about a celestial body, such as a planet, a star, or a comet.

1. Which celestial body will you write about? Choose one that you know well.

   _____

2. Strong informational writing begins with a *hook* that grabs the attention and interest of readers. Write a hook to begin your paragraph.

   _____
   _____
   _____

3. A *topic sentence* expresses the main idea of a paragraph. Write a topic sentence for your paragraph.

   _____
   _____
   _____

4. What information will you include to support your topic sentence? Describe at least three supporting ideas in the order that you'll write them. You do not need to research these ideas at this time.

a. _____

_____

b. _____

_____

c. _____

_____

There are at least 100 billion stars in the Milky Way. Which should I pick?

GET READY

Informational Writing (B)

Spelling List 9 Activity Bank

Circle any words in the box that you did not spell correctly on the pretest. Using your circled words, complete one activity of your choice. Complete as much of the activity as you can in the time given.

If you spelled all words correctly on the pretest, complete your chosen activity with as many spelling words as you can.

aisle	fourth	assistants	rein	millionaire
I'll	mayor	rain	vein	reservoir
isle	mare	reign	vain	turquoise
forth	assistance			

Spelling Activity Choices

Vowel-Free Words

1. In the left column, write only the consonants in each word and put a dot where each vowel should be.

2. Spell each word out loud, stating which vowels should be in the places you wrote dots.

3. In the right column, rewrite the entire spelling word.

4. Correct any spelling errors.

INFORMATIONAL WRITING (B) **155**

Alphabetizing

1. In the left column, write your words from the spelling word list in alphabetical order.

2. Correct any spelling errors.

Parts of Speech

1. In the left column, write the words from your spelling list that are nouns.

2. In the right column, write all the other words from your spelling list and label each word's part of speech.

3. Correct any spelling errors.

Uppercase and Lowercase

1. In the left column, write each of your words in all capital letters, or all uppercase.

2. In the right column, write each of your words in all lowercase letters.

3. Correct any spelling errors.

● **Complete the activity that you chose.**

My chosen activity: _____

1. _____
2. _____
3. _____
4. _____
5. _____
6. _____
7. _____
8. _____
9. _____
10. _____
11. _____
12. _____
13. _____
14. _____
15. _____
16. _____
17. _____
18. _____
19. _____
20. _____
21. _____
22. _____
23. _____
24. _____
_____

TRY IT

Informational Writing Skills (B)

Develop Your Topic

Write your response in complete sentences.

Prompt: Write an informational paragraph about a celestial body.

Write your informational paragraph:

- Write a title.
- Write your hook and topic sentence.
- Write your supporting ideas. Use facts, details, quotations, definitions, and examples to develop your ideas. If needed, research your ideas using a reliable website or other reference.
- Describe, sketch, or paste a copy of an image that would help readers understand your paragraph.

TRY IT

Informational Writing Skills (C)

Clear Up and Conclude Your Paragraph

Use the prompt to answer the questions

Prompt: Write an informational paragraph about a celestial body.

1. Choose at least one sentence from your paragraph that you can revise to use domain-specific language. For instance, you might use the terms *observe*, *orbit*, or *illuminate*. Revise that sentence.

   a. Original sentence:

   _____
   _____

   b. Revised sentence:

   _____
   _____

2. Choose at least one sentence from your paragraph that you can revise to use more precise language. For example, you might name a specific material or tool.

   a. Original sentence:

   _____
   _____

   b. Revised sentence:

   _____
   _____

3. Choose at least one sentence from your paragraph that you can revise to include a transition.

   a. Original sentence:

   _____
   _____

   b. Revised sentence:

   _____
   _____

4. Write a concluding sentence for your paragraph. The conclusion should wrap up the text and stress its overall meaning or importance.

   _____
   _____

I hope my paragraph is *stellar*.

TRY IT

Informational Writing Skills Wrap-Up

Use Informational Writing Skills

Use the prompt and the facts to answer the questions.

Prompt: Write an informational paragraph about the International Space Station.

Facts:

- Travels at 5 miles per second
- Orbits (circles) the earth once every 90 minutes, or 16 times each day
- 16 countries helped build it
- Travels about 250 miles above the earth
- Built in space
- Russia launched first piece in 1998
- Astronauts live onboard
- First astronauts moved in on November 2, 2000
- Astronauts continued to add pieces to the space station
- Finally completed in 2011
- Scientists onboard perform experiments inside and outside of the space station

1. A hook grabs readers' attention. Write a hook to begin your informational paragraph about the International Space Station.

   _____
   _____
   _____

2. The topic sentence states the main idea of the paragraph. Write a topic sentence that states the main idea of your informational paragraph.

   _____
   _____
   _____

3. Using the facts provided, write at least three sentences to support your main idea. You do not need to include every fact.

   _____
   _____
   _____
   _____
   _____
   _____
   _____
   _____

4. Transitions connect and relate ideas in an informational text.

   a. List at least one transition you included in your answer to Question 3.

   _____
   _____
   _____

   b. Explain how the transition improves reader understanding.

   _____
   _____
   _____

5. An informational paragraph uses precise language.

   a. Rewrite one sentence in your paragraph to make the language more precise.

   _____
   _____
   _____

   b. Rewrite at least one sentence in your paragraph to language that is domain-specific.

   _____
   _____
   _____

6. Write a short conclusion to your paragraph. Your conclusion should help readers understand why your main idea is important.

_____
_____
_____
_____

7. Informational writing often contains graphics. These graphics help readers understand the subject or give them a clear mental picture of people or events. Describe one helpful graphic that you could include in your informational paragraph about the International Space Station.

_____
_____
_____

This picture will help clarify my ideas.

TRY IT
Figurative Language

Apply: Comparisons and Sound Words

Choose the word or phrase that best fills in the blank and explain your choice. Think about context clues and what they suggest about the missing word or phrase.

1. Megan is incredibly fast. The race had hardly started and suddenly she was going _____ right across the finish line.

   Would you choose *pitter patter* or *whoosh* to complete this sentence? Why?

   _____
   _____

2. Jimmy really is _____ . He carried my bike, a baseball bat, and a bag of groceries in from outside all by himself in one trip.

   Would you choose *quick like lightning* or *strong as an ox* to complete this sentence? Why?

   _____
   _____

3. It looked like installing the new washing machine was going to be _____ , but then my screwdriver got lost and the power went out.

   Would you choose *a breeze* or *whoosh* to complete this sentence? Why?

   _____
   _____

Write your own sentence using the type of figurative language indicated in each item. Have someone else read your sentence.

4. Onomatopoeia:
   _____
   _____

   Ask your reader to identify the onomatopoeia and tell you whether it captures the sound you intended it to imitate. Discuss his or her answer.

5. A simile:
   _____
   _____

   Ask your reader to identify the simile and explain its meaning. Discuss his or her answer.

6. A metaphor:
   _____
   _____

   Ask your reader to identify the metaphor and explain its meaning. Discuss his or her answer.

My hand is on fire after writing all those metaphors!

168 FIGURATIVE LANGUAGE

GET READY

You Should Meet Katherine Johnson (A)

Spelling List 10 Pretest

1. Open the Spelling Pretest activity online. Listen to the first spelling word. Type the word. Check your answer.

2. Write the correct spelling of the word in the Word column of the Spelling Pretest table on the next page.

	Word	✓	✗
1	blindfold		

3. Put a check mark in the ✓ column if you spelled the word correctly online.

	Word	✓	✗
1	blindfold	✓	

   Put an X in the ✗ column if you spelled the word incorrectly online.

	Word	✓	✗
1	blindfold		X

4. Repeat Steps 1–3 for the remaining words in the Spelling Pretest.

You Should Meet Katherine Johnson (A)

Spelling List 10 Pretest

Write each spelling word in the Word column, making sure to spell it correctly.

#	Word	✓	✗
1			
2			
3			
4			
5			
6			
7			
8			
9			

#	Word	✓	✗
10			
11			
12			
13			
14			
15			
16			
17			

TRY IT

You Should Meet Katherine Johnson (A)

Create a Time Line, Chapters 1–3

Review what you have read in Chapters 1–3 of *You Should Meet Katherine Johnson*. Then choose three sentences from each chapter that contain key details. Write those sentences in chronological order, placing them within quotation marks, on the lines provided. Be sure to copy the sentences exactly. When you are finished, you should have a time line in quotations from the first three chapters of the book.

Chapter 1

_____
_____
_____

Chapter 2

_____
_____
_____

Chapter 3

_____
_____
_____

GET READY
You Should Meet Katherine Johnson (B)

Spelling List 10 Activity Bank

Circle any words in the box that you did not spell correctly on the pretest. Using your circled words, complete one activity of your choice. Complete as much of the activity as you can in the time given.

If you spelled all words correctly on the pretest, complete your chosen activity with as many spelling words as you can.

congregate	inform	persuade	prevention	all right
congregation	information	persuasion	propose	a lot
erode	obsess	prevent	proposition	a while
erosion	obsession			

Spelling Activity Choices

Silly Sentences

1. Write a silly sentence using your words from the spelling word list.

2. Underline the spelling word in each sentence.
   Example: The dog was driving a car.

3. Correct any spelling errors.

Spelling Story

1. Write a very short story using your words from the spelling word list.

2. Underline the spelling words in the story.

3. Correct any spelling errors.

Riddle Me This

1. Write a riddle for your words from the spelling word list.
   Example: "I have a trunk, but it's not on my car."

2. Write the answer, which is your word, for each riddle.
   Example: Answer: elephant

3. Correct any spelling errors.

RunOnWord

1. Gather some crayons, colored pencils, or markers. Write each of your words, using a different color for each word, end to end as one long word.
   Example: dogcatbirdfishturtle

2. Rewrite the words correctly and with proper spacing.

Complete the activity that you chose.

My chosen activity: _____

TRY IT

You Should Meet Katherine Johnson (B)

Create a Time Line, Chapters 4–5

Review what you have read in Chapters 4–5 of *You Should Meet Katherine Johnson*. Then choose three sentences from each chapter that contain key details. Write those sentences in chronological order, placing them within quotation marks, on the lines provided. Be sure to copy the sentences exactly. When you are finished, you should have a time line in quotations from the final two chapters of the book.

Chapter 4

_____
_____
_____
_____

Chapter 5

_____
_____
_____
_____

Gather the time line you created for Chapters 1–3. Use it and the time line you created for Chapters 4–5 to respond to the prompt.

Write a short summary of *You Should Meet Katherine Johnson*. Be sure to include the most important events from Thea Feldman's book. Your summary should be written in complete sentences, and it should describe events in chronological order.

_____
_____
_____
_____
_____
_____
_____
_____
_____
_____
_____
_____
_____
_____
_____
_____
_____
_____
_____

TRY IT

You Should Meet Katherine Johnson (C)

Write About Katherine Johnson

Write your response in complete sentences in the space provided.

Based on your reading in this workshop, what do you think Katherine Johnson's most important accomplishment was? Describe that accomplishment and explain its importance. In your description, include at least one direct quotation from one of the texts you read.

TRY IT

You Should Meet Katherine Johnson Wrap-Up

Write a Review

Write your response in complete sentences in the space provided.

You have read three pieces about Katherine Johnson in this workshop. Choose one of those works and write a review of it now. In your review, be sure to do the following:

- State at least one main idea of the piece.
- Include at least two key details that support the main idea.
- Quote directly and accurately from the text to support one of your points.
- Explain how the piece you chose is different from the others you read in this workshop.

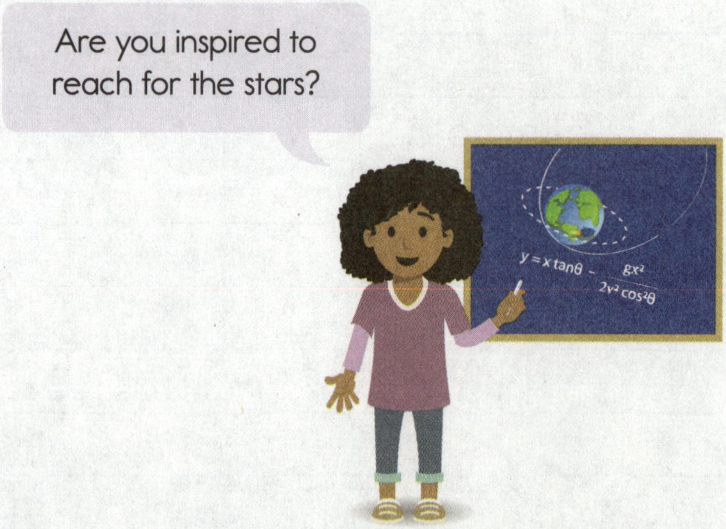
Are you inspired to reach for the stars?
y = x tanθ − gx²/2v² cos²θ

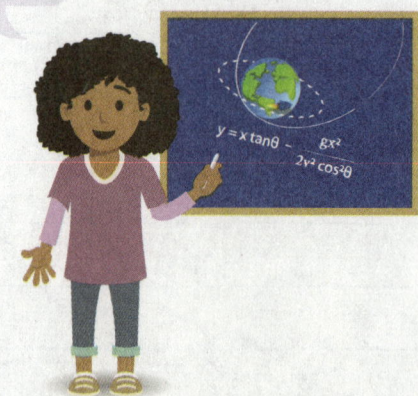

GET READY

Informational Writing: Prewriting (A)

Spelling List 11 Pretest

1. Open the Spelling Pretest activity online. Listen to the first spelling word. Type the word. Check your answer.

2. Write the correct spelling of the word in the Word column of the Spelling Pretest table on the next page.

	WORD	✓	✗
1	blindfold		

3. Put a check mark in the ✓ column if you spelled the word correctly online.

	WORD	✓	✗
1	blindfold	✓	

Put an X in the ✗ column if you spelled the word incorrectly online.

	WORD	✓	✗
1	blindfold		X

4. Repeat Steps 1–3 for the remaining words in the Spelling Pretest.

Informational Writing: Prewriting (A)

Spelling List 11 Pretest

Write each spelling word in the Word column, making sure to spell it correctly.

WORD	✓	✗
1		
2		
3		
4		
5		
6		
7		
8		
9		
10		
11		

WORD	✓	✗
12		
13		
14		
15		
16		
17		
18		
19		
20		
21		

Writing: Prewriting (A)

Your Science Report

assignment. You will complete the assignment in
ble lessons.

a report on a science-related topic.

Your report should have the following:

ction that names the topic and includes relevant background

paragraphs with important facts and details

that sums up key points and wraps up the text

separate different sections of text and briefly describe
hat follows will address

overed during research, including at least one **direct**

illustration, **chart**, or **multimedia element**, such as a

in-specific language and **transitions** to connect and

usage, and **mechanics**

ree **credible sources**, one of which is a print source,
er, magazine, book, or encyclopedia

cher and peers

explain your topic to readers.

rds long (approximately 6–8 handwritten drafting
–2 pages typed and double-spaced)

Brainstorm and choose a topic for your science report. As you brainstorm, you may add more circles to the web.

1. In the circles connected to "Science Report," name at least three broad science categories that interest you. Examples of broad categories are *robotics* and *space exploration*.

2. In the circles connected to each broad category, name at least two topics related to that category. Examples of topics are *water on Mars* and *comets*.

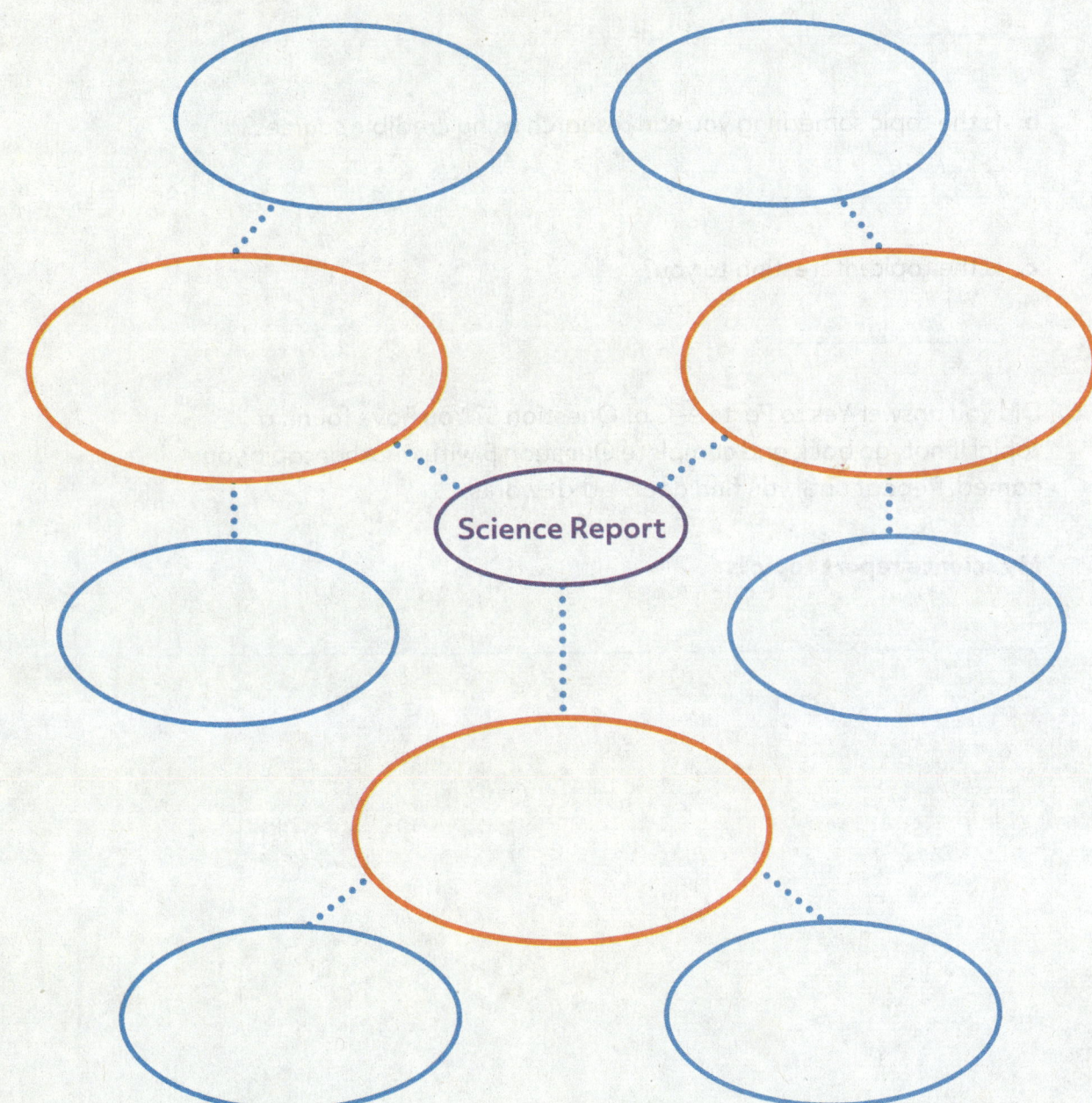

INFORMATIONAL WRITING: PREWRITING (A) 187

3. Read your topics. Cross off topics that seem too large or too broad to cover. Cross off topics that are too small or too narrow.

4. Circle any topics that you really would like to write about. If you didn't circle any topics, add a few more.

5. Choose your favorite topic that you circled. Then answer Yes or No to each question.

   a. Is the topic focused enough to cover in detail in two pages?

   _____

   b. Is the topic something you can research using credible sources?

   _____

   c. Is the topic interesting to you?

   _____

6. Did you answer Yes to Parts A–C of Question 5? You have found a topic! If not, go back and complete Question 5 with another topic you named. Repeat until you find a topic that works.

   My science report topic is

   _____

GET READY

Informational Writing: Prewriting (B)

Spelling List 11 Activity Bank

Circle any words in the box that you did not spell correctly on the pretest. Using your circled words, complete one activity of your choice. Complete as much of the activity as you can in the time given.

If you spelled all words correctly on the pretest, complete your chosen activity with as many spelling words as you can.

brochure	parachute	unique	scenery	crochet
chef	antique	critique	scepter	outgoing
chivalry	plaque	adolescent	scenic	outreach
chute	technique	ascend	chandelier	outspoken
mustache				

Spelling Activity Choices

Hidden Words

1. Draw a picture and "hide" as many words from the Spelling Word List inside the picture as you can.
2. See if others can find the words within the picture.

Triangle Spelling

Write each word in a triangle.

Ghost Words

1. Use a white crayon to write each spelling word.
2. Go over the white crayon writing with a colored marker.

INFORMATIONAL WRITING: PREWRITING (B)

Complete the activity that you chose.

My chosen activity: _____

190 INFORMATIONAL WRITING: PREWRITING (B)

TRY IT

Informational Writing: Prewriting (B)

Research Your Science Report

Follow these steps to write a research question.

1. A research question is the question that you will work to answer in your science report.

   Write three possible research questions for your science report.

   a. _____

   b. _____

   c. _____

2. Choose the research question that most interests you. Be sure that the question is one that you can answer in a 1–2 page report.

My research question:

_____

Follow these steps to conduct research. Record information on the Research Notes pages that follow, using one page per source.

3. Gather or identify at least three sources. At least one source must be a print source, such as a book, an article originally published in a newspaper or magazine, or an encyclopedia article. The other sources may be digital sources found on the Internet. Record the title, author, publisher, and URL of each source.

4. As you read each source, take notes related to your topic and your research question. Paraphrase or summarize from the source. If you find a direct quotation that you think you might use in your report, record the quotation, word for word, in quotation marks. Also record the name of the person you are quoting. Remember, you must use at least one direct quotation in your report.

Research Notes

Source

Title: _____

Author: _____

Published by: _____

URL (if necessary): _____

Notes

Paraphrase/Summary of Key Information:

_____
_____
_____
_____
_____
_____

Direct quotation:

_____
_____
_____

Person quoted: _____

Research Notes

Source

Title: _____

Author: _____

Published by: _____

URL (if necessary): _____

Notes

Paraphrase/Summary of Key Information:
_____
_____
_____
_____
_____
_____

Direct quotation:
_____
_____
_____

Person quoted: _____

Research Notes

Source

Title: _____

Author: _____

Published by: _____

URL (if necessary): _____

Notes

Paraphrase/Summary of Key Information:

_____
_____
_____
_____
_____
_____

Direct quotation:

_____
_____
_____

Person quoted: _____

TRY IT

Informational Writing: Prewriting (C)

Outline for Your Science Report

Use your research notes to complete an outline for your science report. You do not need to use complete sentences in your outline.

Note: Your report must include at least one direct quotation and one piece of media, such as a picture, chart, or video clip. You only need to fill in one blank labeled "Direct Quotation" and one blank labeled "Possible Use of Multimedia" in your outline.

Report Title: _____

Introduction: _____
_____

Hook: _____

Background: _____
_____
_____
_____

Thesis Statement: _____
_____
_____

Body Paragraph 1

Subtopic: _____

Related Information/Details: _____
_____
_____
_____

Direct Quotation (if appropriate): _____
_____

Image or Media (if appropriate) _____
_____

Body Paragraph 2

Subtopic: _____

Related Information/Details: _____
_____
_____
_____

Direct Quotation (if appropriate): _____
_____

Image or Media (if appropriate) _____
_____

Body Paragraph 3

Subtopic: _____

Related Information/Details: _____
_____
_____
_____
_____

Direct Quotation (if appropriate): _____
_____

Image or Media (if appropriate) _____
_____

Conclusion

Closing thoughts: _____
_____

Short summary of key points: _____
_____
_____
_____

Closing thoughts: _____
_____

TRY IT

Informational Writing: Drafting (A)

Draft Your Science Report

Using your notes and your outline to guide you, write the first draft of your science report. Write only on the white rows. You will use the purple rows for revisions later.

Title _____

start here ▶

keep writing ▶

Draft Page 1

keep writing ▶

Draft Page 2

keep writing ▶

Draft Page 3

Draft Page 4

GET READY
Hidden Figures (A)

Spelling List 12 Pretest

1. Open the Spelling Pretest activity online. Listen to the first spelling word. Type the word. Check your answer.

2. Write the correct spelling of the word in the Word column of the Spelling Pretest table on the next page.

#	WORD	✓	✗
1	blindfold		

3. Put a check mark in the ✓ column if you spelled the word correctly online.

#	WORD	✓	✗
1	blindfold	✓	

Put an X in the ✗ column if you spelled the word incorrectly online.

#	WORD	✓	✗
1	blindfold		X

4. Repeat Steps 1–3 for the remaining words in the Spelling Pretest.

Hidden Figures (A)

Spelling List 12 Pretest

Write each spelling word in the Word column, making sure to spell it correctly.

	WORD	✓	✗
1			
2			
3			
4			
5			
6			
7			
8			
9			
10			
11			

	WORD	✓	✗
12			
13			
14			
15			
16			
17			
18			
19			
20			
21			

TRY IT

Hidden Figures (A)

Write About Miriam Mann

Write your response in complete sentences.

Describe the actions of Miriam Mann in Chapter 6 of *Hidden Figures*. Does Margot Lee Shetterly depict Mann's behavior positively or negatively? What details from the text affect your understanding of Mann's behavior? Include at least one direct quotation from *Hidden Figures* to support your answer.

GET READY
Hidden Figures (B)

Spelling List 12 Activity Bank

Circle any words in the box that you did not spell correctly on the pretest. Using your circled words, complete one activity of your choice. Complete as much of the activity as you can in the time given.

If you spelled all words correctly on the pretest, complete your chosen activity with as many spelling words as you can.

define	personal	related	know	overturn
definite	personality	relative	knowledge	abbreviate
definition	practical	soft	overreach	abbreviation
oppose	practice	soften	override	brevity
opposite				

Spelling Activity Choices

Create a Crossword

1. Write a word from your spelling word list in the center of the grid paper.

2. Write another spelling word going across and sharing a letter with the first word. See how many words you can connect.

   Example:

			p				
		k	i	s	s	e	s
	d		n				
r	o	c	k	s			
	g						
	s						

Word Search Puzzle

1. Draw a box on the grid paper. The box should be large enough to hold your words from the spelling word list.

2. Fill in the grid paper with words from your spelling list, writing them horizontally, vertically, and diagonally (forwards or backwards if you choose).

3. Fill in the rest of the box with random letters.

4. Ask someone to find and circle your spelling words in the puzzle you made.

- **Complete the activity that you chose.**

  My chosen activity: _____

HIDDEN FIGURES (B)

TRY IT

Hidden Figures (B)

Write About *Hidden Figures*, Chapters 10–12

Write your response in complete sentences.

Compare Mary Jackson and Katherine Goble, who Margot Lee Shetterly focuses on in Chapters 10–12 *Hidden Figures*. How were the two women alike, both in terms of their personalities and their experiences? What incidents show why both were successful at NACA? How does their success shape your understanding of this book? Include at least one direct quotation from *Hidden Figures* to support your answer.

TRY IT

Hidden Figures (C)

Write About Women at NASA Then and Now

Write your response in complete sentences.

Based on what you read in *Hidden Figures* and in the article "NASA Langley's Modern Figures Reflect on Changing Times and *Hidden Figures*," how has the experience of being a NASA professional who is not a white male changed over the last 75 years? How has it stayed the same? Integrate, or combine, information from both texts in your response. Also include at least one direct quotation from one of the texts you read.

How will working at NASA change in the future?

TRY IT

Hidden Figures Wrap-Up

Write About *Hidden Figures*

Write your responses in complete sentences in the space provided.

You have read several chapters from Margot Lee Shetterly's *Hidden Figures*, as well as additional articles about some of the women in the book.

- After reading and reflecting on these works, briefly explain why reading them is a valuable experience.
- What did you gain from reading about these women?
- Which parts of the readings did you find most meaningful or interesting? Why?
- How did reading more than one text on the same subject affect your understanding of it?
- Be sure to include at least one direct quotation from a text in this workshop in your response

GET READY

"A Ride in the Night"

Spelling List 13 Pretest

1. Open the Spelling Pretest activity online. Listen to the first spelling word. Type the word. Check your answer.

2. Write the correct spelling of the word in the Word column of the Spelling Pretest table on the next page.

	Word	✓	✗
1	blindfold		

3. Put a check mark in the ✓ column if you spelled the word correctly online.

	Word	✓	✗
1	blindfold	✓	

Put an X in the ✗ column if you spelled the word incorrectly online.

	Word	✓	✗
1	blindfold		X

4. Repeat Steps 1–3 for the remaining words in the Spelling Pretest.

"A Ride in the Night"

Spelling List 13 Pretest

Write each spelling word in the Word column, making sure to spell it correctly.

#	Word	✓	✗
1			
2			
3			
4			
5			
6			
7			
8			
9			

#	Word	✓	✗
10			
11			
12			
13			
14			
15			
16			
17			

TRY IT

"A Ride in the Night"

Write About Will Clark

Read the excerpt from "A Ride in the Night" by Katharine E. Wilkie and answer the questions.

> The soldier called Brown turned toward Will. His eyes were cold and dangerous. He twisted Will's shoulder crudely. "We're on the lookout for horses intended for the Continental Army. Do you know anything about them?"
>
> "Ouch! You're hurting me!"
>
> The man's roughness had brought real tears to Will's eyes. The boy was glad of it. The pain would excuse the look of fear on his face. But his great fear was for York, hidden back in the woods with the horses.

1. What can you infer about Will Clark based on this passage?

   _____
   _____
   _____

2. What evidence in the passage supports your inference?

   _____
   _____
   _____

GET READY

"A Ride in the Night" Wrap-Up

Spelling List 13 Activity Bank

Circle any words in the box that you did not spell correctly on the pretest. Using your circled words, complete one activity of your choice. Complete as much of the activity as you can in the time given.

If you spelled all words correctly on the pretest, complete your chosen activity with as many spelling words as you can.

adapt	affect	conscious	effect	belligerent
adopt	allowed	decent	picture	rebellion
advice	aloud	descent	pitcher	rebellious
advise	conscience			

Spelling Activity Choices

Vowel-Free Words

1. In the left column, write only the consonants in each word and put a dot where each vowel should be.

2. Spell each word out loud, stating which vowels should be in the places you wrote dots.

3. In the right column, rewrite the entire spelling word.

4. Correct any spelling errors.

Alphabetizing

1. In the left column, write your words from the spelling word list in alphabetical order.
2. Correct any spelling errors.

Parts of Speech

1. In the left column, write the words from your spelling list that are nouns.
2. In the right column, write all the other words from your spelling list and label each word's part of speech.
3. Correct any spelling errors.

Uppercase and Lowercase

1. In the left column, write each of your words in all capital letters, or all uppercase.
2. In the right column, write each of your words in all lowercase letters.
3. Correct any spelling errors.

Complete the activity that you chose.

My chosen activity: _____

1. _____   _____
2. _____   _____
3. _____   _____
4. _____   _____
5. _____   _____
6. _____   _____
7. _____   _____
8. _____   _____
9. _____   _____
10. _____   _____
11. _____   _____
12. _____   _____
13. _____   _____
14. _____   _____
15. _____   _____
16. _____   _____
17. _____   _____
18. _____   _____
19. _____   _____
20. _____   _____
21. _____   _____
22. _____   _____
23. _____   _____
24. _____   _____
_____

TRY IT
"A Ride in the Night" Wrap-Up

Write About "A Ride in the Night"

A summary is a short retelling of the most important ideas or events in a text. Good summaries describe events in the same order as the text they summarize.

Summarize "A Ride in the Night" in two or three paragraphs.

TRY IT
"Run, Kate Shelley, Run"

Write About Key Details and Main Ideas

Read the excerpt from "Run, Kate Shelley, Run" by Julia Pferdehirt and answer the questions.

When she saw the station lights, Kate ran like a wild woman. Her wet skirt slapped and caught against her legs. Every breath hurt. She crashed into the station door and fell inside.

"Stop! Stop the train!" she gasped. "The engine—Honey Creek. Stop the train."

"The girl's crazy!" said one of the railroad men.

"Not on your life!" said the station agent. "That's Shelley's girl Kate."

Between gasps of air, Kate told them the Honey Creek Bridge had collapsed. "Two men are still alive," she said. "And the midnight express must be stopped."

1. What are some of the key details in this passage?

_____
_____
_____
_____
_____

2. What is one main idea that you can infer based on the key details you identified?

_____
_____
_____
_____
_____
_____

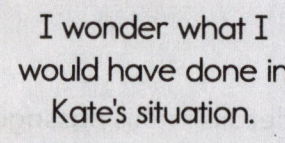
I wonder what I would have done in Kate's situation.

TRY IT

"Run, Kate Shelley, Run" Wrap-Up

Write About "Run, Kate Shelley, Run"

Good summaries retell only the most important ideas or events in a text. They leave out minor or unimportant details, and they follow the same order as the text they summarize.

Summarize "Run, Kate Shelley, Run" in two or three paragraphs.

TRY IT

Informational Writing: Revising

Revise Your Science Report

Use the checklist as you revise your science report draft.

Organization

☐ Does my report have an introduction, at least three body paragraphs, and a conclusion?

☐ Does my introduction clearly state the topic?

☐ Are supporting ideas grouped in the correct body paragraphs?

☐ Do appropriate headings separate the different sections of my report?

☐ Do I use clear and logical transitions?

Content

☐ Is my report factual and well researched, showing that I understand the topic?

☐ Do I use enough facts and supporting details, including at least one quotation, to explain ideas?

☐ Does my conclusion make sense and answer important questions?

☐ Are the words I use precise and domain-specific?

☐ Do I have a source list that includes at least three research sources, one of which is a print source?

TRY IT

Informational Writing: Proofreading

Proofread Your Science Report

Use the checklist as you proofread your science report draft.

Grammar and Usage

☐ Are all sentences complete and correct?

☐ Are there any missing or extra words?

☐ Are conjunctions, prepositions, and interjections used correctly and effectively?

☐ Are there other grammatical or usage errors?

Mechanics

☐ Is every word spelled correctly, including frequently confused words?

☐ Does every sentence begin with a capital letter and end with the appropriate punctuation?

☐ Are direct quotations punctuated correctly?

☐ Are titles of works formatted correctly?

☐ Are there other punctuation or capitalization errors?

TRY IT

Greek Roots and Affixes

Apply: Greek Roots and Affixes

Read the paragraph. Think about context clues and what they suggest about the missing word or phrase.

1. We've spent a long time trying to stop our dog's _____ bad behavior, but he still won't obey. He spends most days chewing our shoes and most nights howling. He's acted this way since he was a puppy.

   a. Which word correctly fills in the blank? *chronic* or *chronological*

   b. Explanation:

   _____
   _____

2. My grandfather's pocket watch is dented on the outside and its face is cracked, but it is still ticking. I guess that's why I think of the watch as a _____ of my grandfather himself. Just like his watch, he isn't in perfect condition, but he's still going.

   a. Which word correctly fills in the blank? *symphony* or *symbol*

   b. Explanation:

   _____
   _____

3. When I turned on the TV, the first thing I saw was a _____ that showed the outline of a woman on a snowboard. Right away, I remembered that the Winter Olympics had started the day before.

   a. Which word correctly fills in the blank? *biography* or *graphic*

   b. Explanation:

   _____

   _____

Write a sentence using a word that comes from the given Greek root.

- **Have someone else read your sentence.**
- **Explain to this person how the meaning of your word relates to the meaning of the given Greek root.**
- **Explain how any affixes that are part of your word affect the word's meaning.**

4. *chron*

   Sentence:

   _____

   _____

5. *sym*

   Sentence:

   _____

   _____

6. *graph*

   Sentence:

   _____

   _____

GET READY

"Young Frederick Douglass"

Spelling List 14 Pretest

1. Open the Spelling Pretest activity online. Listen to the first spelling word. Type the word. Check your answer.

2. Write the correct spelling of the word in the Word column of the Spelling Pretest table on the next page.

	Word	✓	✗
1	blindfold		

3. Put a check mark in the ✓ column if you spelled the word correctly online.

	Word	✓	✗
1	blindfold	✓	

Put an X in the ✗ column if you spelled the word incorrectly online.

	Word	✓	✗
1	blindfold		X

4. Repeat Steps 1–3 for the remaining words in the Spelling Pretest.

"Young Frederick Douglass"

Spelling List 14 Pretest

Write each spelling word in the Word column, making sure to spell it correctly.

#	Word	✓	✗
1			
2			
3			
4			
5			
6			
7			
8			
9			

#	Word	✓	✗
10			
11			
12			
13			
14			
15			
16			
17			

TRY IT

"Young Frederick Douglass"

Write About Multiple Main Ideas

Read the excerpt from "Young Frederick Douglass: The Slave Who Learned to Read" by Linda Walvoord Girard and answer the questions.

> When other slaves in St. Michael's learned that Frederick could read, they asked him to teach a Sunday school. The class met secretly in a free black man's house where there were desks, spelling books, and Bibles. During the second week, Thomas Auld burst in with a white mob. The men broke up the school with clubs and warned the students never to meet again.

1. What is one main idea of this passage?
   _____
   _____
   _____

2. What key details support or help convey this main idea?
   _____
   _____
   _____

3. What is a second main idea of this passage?

   _____
   _____
   _____

4. What key details support or help convey this second main idea?

   _____
   _____
   _____

GET READY

"Young Frederick Douglass" Wrap-Up

Spelling List 14 Activity Bank

Circle any words in the box that you did not spell correctly on the pretest. Using your circled words, complete one activity of your choice. Complete as much of the activity as you can in the time given.

If you spelled all words correctly on the pretest, complete your chosen activity with as many spelling words as you can.

echoes	vetoes	videos	knives	shelves
heroes	patios	zoos	loaves	wives
potatoes	radios	calves	scarves	wolves
tomatoes	studios			

Spelling Activity Choices

Silly Sentences

1. Write a silly sentence using your words from the spelling word list.

2. Underline the spelling word in each sentence.
   Example: The dog was driving a car.

3. Correct any spelling errors.

Spelling Story

1. Write a very short story using your words from the spelling word list.

2. Underline the spelling words in the story.

3. Correct any spelling errors.

Riddle Me This

1. Write a riddle for your words from the spelling word list.
   Example: "I have a trunk, but it's not on my car."

2. Write the answer, which is your word, for each riddle.
   Example: Answer: elephant

3. Correct any spelling errors.

RunOnWord

1. Gather some crayons, colored pencils, or markers. Write each of your words, using a different color for each word, end to end as one long word.
   Example: dogcatbirdfishturtle

2. Rewrite the words correctly and with proper spacing.

- **Complete the activity that you chose.**

  My chosen activity: _____

"YOUNG FREDERICK DOUGLASS" WRAP-UP

TRY IT

"Young Frederick Douglass" Wrap-Up

Write About "Young Frederick Douglass"

Strong summaries briefly retell the most important ideas or events in a text. They describe events in the same order as the original text.

Summarize "Young Frederick Douglass: The Slave Who Learned to Read" in two or three paragraphs.

TRY IT

"The Most Famous Woman in America"

Write About Facts and Opinions

Each line is from "The Most Famous Woman in America."

Write "Fact" if the line states a fact and "Opinion" if the line expresses an opinion.

1. Aid stations were now set up near every battlefield.

   _____

2. "There has never been anyone like her in this world," said one old man.

   _____

3. "She obtained permission to join the Army of the Potomac in 1862."

   _____

4. Again she was the most famous woman in the United States.

   _____

5. For Questions 1 through 4, how do you know which lines are facts and which lines are opinions?

   _____
   _____
   _____
   _____

6. What is one main idea of "The Most Famous Woman in America"?

   _____
   _____
   _____

7. What are two key details that support the main idea you identified?

   _____
   _____
   _____

What can I do to change the world for the better?

TRY IT

"The Most Famous Woman in America" Wrap-Up

Write About "The Most Famous Woman in America"

Answer the questions in complete sentences.

1. What is one fact you learned about Clara Barton from reading "The Most Famous Woman in America"? How do you know that this is a fact?

   _____
   _____
   _____
   _____
   _____

2. What is one opinion you have about Clara Barton after reading "The Most Famous Woman in America"? What made you form this opinion about Barton?

   _____
   _____
   _____
   _____
   _____

GET READY

Microscopes (A)

Spelling List 15 Pretest

1. Open the Spelling Pretest activity online. Listen to the first spelling word. Type the word. Check your answer.

2. Write the correct spelling of the word in the Word column of the Spelling Pretest table on the next page.

	Word	✓	✗
1	blindfold		

3. Put a check mark in the ✓ column if you spelled the word correctly online.

	Word	✓	✗
1	blindfold	✓	

Put an X in the ✗ column if you spelled the word incorrectly online.

	Word	✓	✗
1	blindfold		X

4. Repeat Steps 1–3 for the remaining words in the Spelling Pretest.

Microscopes (A)

Spelling List 15 Pretest

Write each spelling word in the Word column, making sure to spell it correctly.

#	Word	✓	✗
1			
2			
3			
4			
5			
6			
7			
8			
9			

#	Word	✓	✗
10			
11			
12			
13			
14			
15			
16			
17			

TRY IT

Microscopes (A)

Write About the Author's Beliefs

Read the passage from "Make Your Own Microscope."
Write your response in complete sentences.

> Finally, this whole process left me with a terrific tool. In some ways, my new smartphone microscope is just as good as my old microscope. In other ways, it's even better. For example, just like with my old microscope, I can enlarge whatever I am observing to an image up to 175 times its actual size. That is more than powerful enough to view the crystal structure of salt or the brickwork pattern of skin cells. But there's also the fact that my smartphone microscope is light. It's portable. I can take it with me anywhere. Plus, using its video function, I can even record whatever I'm looking at. That means I can capture motion and changes over time. Next week, I'm going to look at some pond water and record the movement of the bacteria in it. I couldn't do anything like that with my old, heavy microscope!

Now write at least one paragraph in which you

- State one belief that the author expresses in the passage.
- Explain why the author believes what she does, citing at least one detail from the text that supports her belief.
- Describe how the author's statement of her belief affects the text and readers.

GET READY
Microscopes (B)

Spelling List 15 Activity Bank

Circle any words in the box that you did not spell correctly on the pretest. Using your circled words, complete one activity of your choice. Complete as much of the activity as you can in the time given.

If you spelled all words correctly on the pretest, complete your chosen activity with as many spelling words as you can.

angered	mattered	deferring	propelling	canceled
covering	sheltered	occurring	rebelled	traveled
gathering	suffering	preferred	referring	altering
labeled	concurred			

Spelling Activity Choices

Hidden Words

1. Draw a picture and "hide" as many words from the Spelling Word List inside the picture as you can.
2. See if others can find the words within the picture.

Triangle Spelling

Write each word in a triangle.

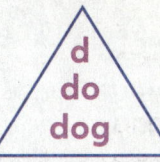

Ghost Words

1. Use a white crayon to write each spelling word.
2. Go over the white crayon writing with a colored marker.

Complete the activity that you chose.

My chosen activity: _____

256 MICROSCOPES (B)

TRY IT
Microscopes (B)

Paraphrase a Passage

Read the passage from "Stick to Real Microscopes."
Write your response in complete sentences.

The most powerful smartphone microscopes can magnify objects up to 350 times their actual size. That sounds impressive. But it pales in comparison to what a real microscope can do. A mid-level real microscope can magnify objects up to 2,000 times their actual size. Let those numbers sink it. They say that a real microscope is five to six times more powerful than a smartphone microscope.

And what does that mean in the lab? Well, imagine looking at a sample of blood. With a real microscope, one would see individual red blood cells, their specific shapes, and their distinct movements. A smartphone microscope would give the observer a very different picture. Suddenly, the sample would look like just a hazy collection of tiny red blobs (Manea). Remember, scientists seek to gather precise and accurate information. But the information gathered with the smartphone microscope would be less precise and less accurate. It would be less useful. Again, when the two are compared, the smartphone microscope comes up short.

Now paraphrase the passage. As you write

- Identify key ideas and details in the passage.
- Present these key ideas and details accurately, but in your own words.
- Name the source of the paraphrase's information.
- Maintain the order of the passage.

_____
_____
_____
_____
_____
_____
_____
_____
_____

TRY IT

Microscopes (C)

Plan to Write About Microscopes

Read the directions and complete the graphic organizer.

Now that you have read and analyzed two opinion pieces about microscopes, you are almost ready to write about them. First, you will plan your writing.

To do so, complete a graphic organizer. Fill in the first two sections with information from each text. You can and should paraphrase key ideas and note important details. Then complete the last two sections by noting how the texts are similar and how they are different.

When you have finished, save this graphic organizer. You will use it to guide your writing in an upcoming lesson.

"Make Your Own Microscope"

Overall opinion expressed by the text:

_____
_____
_____

Key ideas/details/facts in support of overall opinion:

_____
_____
_____
_____
_____

"Stick to Real Microscopes"

Overall opinion expressed by the text:

_____

_____

_____

Key ideas/details/facts in support of overall opinion:

_____

_____

_____

_____

Similarities Between Texts

Structure:

_____

_____

_____

_____

Ideas:

_____

_____

_____

Differences Between Texts

Structure:
_____
_____
_____
_____

Ideas:
_____
_____
_____

In my opinion, both authors made some great points.

TRY IT
Microscopes Wrap-Up

Write About Microscopes

Read the directions and complete the assignment.

Gather the Plan to Write About Microscopes page that you completed in Microscopes (C). Use the graphic organizer to help you write a four-paragraph essay comparing and contrasting "Make Your Own Microscope" and "Stick to Real Microscopes."

Your essay should follow the structure laid out in the graphic organizer.

- The first two paragraphs should paraphrase and summarize the key ideas and details of each passage.
- The third paragraph should focus on how the structure and ideas of the texts are similar.
- The fourth paragraph should focus on how the structure and ideas of the texts are different.

Write in complete sentences and avoid plagiarism.

_____
_____
_____
_____
_____
_____
_____
_____
_____

TRY IT
Latin Roots and Affixes

Apply: Practice Using Words with Latin Roots

Rewrite the following sentences or add a second sentence that makes the meaning of the underlined word clear. The first one has been done for you.

1. The family lived in a very simple structure.

   New sentence: The family lived in a very simple structure. The building had one room, and each of its four walls had a single window.

2. Are you going to construct a boat out of that?

3. Jesse has a serious malady.

4. The old man on the corner had a malevolent look in his eye.

5. The vandals who broke into the museum last night decided to mutilate the artwork.

GET READY

Opinion Writing Skills (A)

Spelling List 16 Pretest

1. Open the Spelling Pretest activity online. Listen to the first spelling word. Type the word. Check your answer.

2. Write the correct spelling of the word in the Word column of the Spelling Pretest table on the next page.

Word	✓	✗
1 blindfold		

3. Put a check mark in the ✓ column if you spelled the word correctly online.

Word	✓	✗
1 blindfold	✓	

   Put an X in the ✗ column if you spelled the word incorrectly online.

Word	✓	✗
1 blindfold		X

4. Repeat Steps 1–3 for the remaining words in the Spelling Pretest.

Opinion Writing Skills (A)

Spelling List 16 Pretest

Write each spelling word in the Word column, making sure to spell it correctly.

	Word	✓	✗
1			
2			
3			
4			
5			
6			
7			
8			
9			

	Word	✓	✗
10			
11			
12			
13			
14			
15			
16			
17			

TRY IT

Opinion Writing Skills (A)

Begin Your Opinion Piece

Use the prompt to answer the questions.

Prompt: Write about an activity you think everyone should try at least once.

1. Think about the activity you have chosen.

    a. What is the activity?

    _____

    b. Is there important information that the average reader may not know about the activity? For example, does the activity require a certain number of people, or is it only available during a certain time of year?

    _____
    _____
    _____

2. Think about your opinion.

    a. What is your opinion of the activity?

    _____

    b. Determine three reasons to support your opinion. Then consider the most logical and effective way to organize your reasons. Write your reasons in the order you will discuss them in your opinion piece.

OPINION WRITING SKILLS (A) **269**

Reason 1:

_____

Reason 2:

_____

Reason 3:

_____

3. Use your answers to Questions 1 and 2 to write an introduction to your opinion piece. Your introduction should

   - Provide background information about your activity.
   - Clearly state your opinion.
   - List the reasons for your opinion in the order you will write about them.

_____

_____

_____

_____

_____

_____

_____

_____

GET READY

Opinion Writing Skills (B)

Spelling List 16 Activity Bank

Circle any words in the box that you did not spell correctly on the pretest. Using your circled words, complete one activity of your choice. Complete as much of the activity as you can in the time given.

If you spelled all words correctly on the pretest, complete your chosen activity with as many spelling words as you can.

supervision	depression	revision	profession	decline
television	discussion	transfusion	progression	incline
pretension	inclusion	possession	division	recline
confession	impression			

Spelling Activity Choices

Create a Crossword

1. Write a word from your spelling word list in the center of the grid paper.

2. Write another spelling word going across and sharing a letter with the first word. See how many words you can connect.

   Example:

		p				
	k	i	s	s	e	s
d		n				
r	o	c	k	s		
g						
s						

OPINION WRITING SKILLS (B)

Word Search Puzzle

1. Draw a box on the grid paper. The box should be large enough to hold your words from the spelling word list.

2. Fill in the grid paper with words from your spelling list, writing them horizontally, vertically, and diagonally (forward and backward if you choose).

3. Fill in the rest of the box with random letters.

4. Ask someone to find and circle your spelling words in the puzzle you made.

Complete the activity that you chose.

My chosen activity: _____

TRY IT

Opinion Writing Skills (B)

Order Reasons and Provide Evidence

Use the prompt to complete the graphic organizer.

Prompt: Write about an activity you think everyone should try at least once.

1. Write your opinion of the activity you have chosen and three reasons that support your opinion. Organize your reasons in the most logical and effective order. For each reason, list at least two supporting facts or details.

Opinion:

_____

_____

Reason 1:

_____

Supporting facts or details:

- _____
- _____
- _____

Reason 2:

_____

Supporting facts or details:

- _____
- _____
- _____

Reason 3:

_____

Supporting facts or details:

- _____
- _____
- _____

Write your response in complete sentences.

2. How did you choose the order of your reasons? Explain your logic.

   _____
   _____
   _____

TRY IT

Opinion Writing Skills (C)

Link Ideas and Conclude Your Opinion Piece

Use the prompt to answer the questions.

Prompt: Write about an activity you think everyone should try at least once.

1. Write one body paragraph of your opinion piece.

   a. Write a topic sentence that states your first reason. Begin the sentence with a transition that connects that reason to your opinion. Underline the transition.

   _____
   _____
   _____

   b. Write the remainder of that paragraph by supporting your reason with facts and details. Use at least one transition to connect your ideas. Underline the transitions.

   _____
   _____
   _____
   _____
   _____
   _____
   _____

2. Write the conclusion to your opinion piece.
   - Start with a transition, such as "To sum it up," "In conclusion," "All in all," or "As you can see."
   - State your opinion in words that are different from what you wrote in your introduction.
   - Briefly restate the reasons for your opinion.
   - Include any additional thoughts you have about the topic.

TRY IT

Opinion Writing Skills Wrap-Up

Use Opinion Writing Skills

Use the prompt to answer the questions.

Prompt: Would it be better to travel to the past or to the future?

1. Complete the graphic organizer on the next page to show how you would respond to the prompt.

Introduction

State your opinion in response to the prompt.

Reasons

Write three reasons for your opinion in a logical and effective order. Write at least two facts or details to support your first reason.

1.
   -
   -

2.

3.

Conclusion

Write one sentence to conclude your opinion piece. Your sentence should summarize your opinion and reasons.

OPINION WRITING SKILLS WRAP-UP

2. Introducing a topic is an important part of an introduction.

   Look back at your opinion sentence. Imagine that someone reading that sentence is unsure of how far in time you would like to travel or where you would like to go. Revise that sentence or add an additional sentence so that you have fully introduced your topic.

   Revised introduction:

   _____
   _____
   _____

3. Strong writers use transitions to connect reasons to an opinion.

   Rewrite your first reason so that it begins with a transition.

   _____
   _____

I would travel to the future to see my response to the prompt.

OPINION WRITING SKILLS WRAP-UP

GET READY

Solar Power (A)

Spelling List 17 Pretest

1. Open the Spelling Pretest activity online. Listen to the first spelling word. Type the word. Check your answer.

2. Write the correct spelling of the word in the Word column of the Spelling Pretest table on the next page.

Word	✓	✗
1 blindfold		

3. Put a check mark in the ✓ column if you spelled the word correctly online.

Word	✓	✗
1 blindfold	✓	

Put an X in the ✗ column if you spelled the word incorrectly online.

Word	✓	✗
1 blindfold		✗

4. Repeat Steps 1–3 for the remaining words in the Spelling Pretest.

SOLAR POWER (A) 283

Solar Power (A)

Spelling List 17 Pretest

Write each spelling word in the Word column, making sure to spell it correctly.

	Word	✓	✗
1			
2			
3			
4			
5			
6			
7			
8			
9			

	Word	✓	✗
10			
11			
12			
13			
14			
15			
16			
17			

TRY IT
Solar Power (A)

Write About a Persuasive Passage

Read the passage.

Write your response in complete sentences.

> The Olympics are about to begin. For weeks, the world will watch its best athletes compete. It will be thrilling and inspiring. People across the globe will celebrate their nations' best and brightest young stars. And then, just like that, the games will be over. Another four years will pass before they begin again. This is silly! The Olympics should be held every summer.
>
> Holding the Olympics every year would have all kinds of benefits. It would bring people from every country together. It would remind them that they are not so different. It would allow them to build friendships. And, it would ultimately lead to better relations between countries. Who on earth would object to that?

Now write at least one paragraph in which you do the following:

- Identify the writer's position or viewpoint.
- Explain how the writer presents ideas in ways that attempt to sway or convince readers to agree with his position or viewpoint.
- Describe why these ways of presenting ideas are effective.

GET READY

Solar Power (B)

Spelling List 17 Activity Bank

Circle any words in the box that you did not spell correctly on the pretest. Using your circled words, complete one activity of your choice. Complete as much of the activity as you can in the time given.

If you spelled all words correctly on the pretest, complete your chosen activity with as many spelling words as you can.

hour	year	department	govt.	no.
hr.	yr.	dept.	inc.	number
month	co.	government	incorporated	nos.
mo.	company			

Spelling Activity Choices

Vowel-Free Words

1. In the left column, write only the consonants in each word and put a dot where each vowel should be.

2. Spell each word out loud, stating which vowels should be in the places you wrote dots.

3. In the right column, rewrite the entire spelling word.

4. Correct any spelling errors.

Alphabetizing

1. In the left column, write your words from the spelling word list in alphabetical order.
2. Correct any spelling errors.

Parts of Speech

1. In the left column, write the words from your spelling list that are nouns.
2. In the right column, write all the other words from your spelling list and label each word's part of speech.
3. Correct any spelling errors.

Uppercase and Lowercase

1. In the left column, write each of your words in all capital (uppercase) letters.
2. In the right column, write each of your words in all lowercase letters.
3. Correct any spelling errors.

Complete the activity that you chose.

My chosen activity: _____

1. _____ _____
2. _____ _____
3. _____ _____
4. _____ _____
5. _____ _____
6. _____ _____
7. _____ _____
8. _____ _____
9. _____ _____
10. _____ _____
11. _____ _____
12. _____ _____
13. _____ _____
14. _____ _____
15. _____ _____
16. _____ _____
17. _____ _____
18. _____ _____
19. _____ _____
20. _____ _____
21. _____ _____
22. _____ _____
23. _____ _____
24. _____ _____
_____

TRY IT

Solar Power (B)

Write About How a Writer Persuades Readers

Read the passage. Then write your responses in complete sentences.

It's nearly summer, and that means that Fun Zone will soon open its doors. Hopefully, this is the last year that this statement is true. Why? Fun Zone is an overpriced, unsafe amusement park that no one should visit.

Let's start with the cost of visiting Fun Zone, which is outrageous. Adults must pay $120 to get in the front gate. Admission for children is $80. So, it would cost a family of four $400 just to visit Fun Zone. That number doesn't even take into account the fact that food and drinks in the park are wildly expensive. A hot dog costs $9. A bottle of water is $6. Oh, Fun Zone also charges visitors $35 for parking. If you add it all up, a single day at Fun Zone could easily cost that family of four over $500. That's far more than many families in our town can afford to spend.

The high prices aren't the only issue with Fun Zone. The park is also full of dangerous rides. Last year, 50 people were hurt when the Looptacular Roller Coaster hopped the tracks and skidded into the platform. Two women hurt their backs when they slipped on a wet bathroom floor. The Ferris wheel broke down and stranded dozens of visitors more than 100 feet in the air for six hours. And an ostrich escaped from the petting zoo and pecked a little boy's arms, causing bruises and nightmares.

1. What stance or position does the writer take in this passage?

   _____
   _____
   _____

2. How does the writer support his or her position? Cite specific examples from the text.

   _____
   _____
   _____
   _____
   _____

3. Why is the support the writer provides persuasive?

   _____
   _____
   _____
   _____
   _____

TRY IT
Solar Power (C)

Plan to Write About Solar Power

Read the directions and complete the graphic organizer.

Now that you have read and analyzed two persuasive essays about solar power, you are almost ready to write about them. First, you will plan your writing.

To do so, complete a graphic organizer. Fill in the first two sections with information from each text. You can and should paraphrase key ideas and note important details. Then complete the last two sections by noting how the texts are similar and how they are different.

When you have finished, save this graphic organizer. You will use it to guide your writing in an upcoming lesson.

"Solar Power for Public Buildings"

Writer's position:

_____
_____
_____

Key claims/evidence in support of position:

_____
_____
_____
_____

"Not So Fast, California"

Writer's position:
_____
_____
_____

Key claims/evidence in support of position:
_____
_____
_____
_____

Similarities Between Texts

Structure:
_____
_____
_____
_____

Ideas:
_____
_____
_____

Differences Between Texts

Structure:
_____
_____
_____
_____

Ideas:
_____
_____
_____

TRY IT
Solar Power Wrap-Up

Write About Solar Power

Read the directions and complete the assignment.

Gather the Plan to Write About Solar Power page that you completed in Solar Power (C). Use the graphic organizer to help you write a four-paragraph essay comparing and contrasting "Solar Power for Public Buildings" and "Not So Fast, California!"

Your essay should follow the structure laid out in the graphic organizer.

- The first two paragraphs should paraphrase and summarize the key ideas and details of each persuasive essay.
- The third paragraph should focus on how the structure and ideas of the texts are similar.
- The fourth paragraph should focus on how the structure and ideas of the texts are different

Remember to write in complete sentences and avoid plagiarism.

GET READY

Who Is Sonia Sotomayor? (A)

Spelling List 18 Pretest

1. Open the Spelling Pretest activity online. Listen to the first spelling word. Type the word. Check your answer.

2. Write the correct spelling of the word in the Word column of the Spelling Pretest table on the next page.

	Word	✓	✗
1	blindfold		

3. Put a check mark in the ✓ column if you spelled the word correctly online.

	Word	✓	✗
1	blindfold	✓	

Put an X in the ✗ column if you spelled the word incorrectly online.

	Word	✓	✗
1	blindfold		X

4. Repeat Steps 1–3 for the remaining words in the Spelling Pretest.

Who Is Sonia Sotomayor? (A)

Spelling List 18 Pretest

Write each spelling word in the Word column, making sure to spell it correctly.

#	Word	✓	✗
1			
2			
3			
4			
5			
6			
7			
8			
9			
10			
11			
12			
13			

#	Word	✓	✗
14			
15			
16			
17			
18			
19			
20			
21			
22			
23			
24			
25			

TRY IT

Who Is Sonia Sotomayor? (A)

Write About Events in Your Biography

Write your responses in complete sentences.

1. Imagine a biography about your own life. What five events would be included? Why would these events be a part of your biography?

   _____
   _____
   _____
   _____
   _____

2. If you were to write the story of your own life, would it still be a biography? Why or why not? How would the story of your life be different if it were written by another person?

   _____
   _____
   _____
   _____
   _____

GET READY

Who Is Sonia Sotomayor? (B)

Spelling List 18 Activity Bank

Circle any words in the box that you did not spell correctly on the pretest. Using your circled words, complete one activity of your choice. Complete as much of the activity as you can in the time given.

If you spelled all words correctly on the pretest, complete your chosen activity with as many spelling words as you can.

forgiving	bossiness	emptiness	tinier	alphabetical
displaced	homeless	happiness	certain	biographical
replacing	replacement	healthier	certificate	comical
creating	cleanliness	muddier	certify	cubical
wisely	craziness	noisiest	ascertain	typical

Spelling Activity Choices

Silly Sentencess

1. Write a silly sentence using your words from the spelling word list.

2. Underline the spelling word in each sentence.
   Example: The dog was driving a car.

3. Correct any spelling errors.

Spelling Story

1. Write a very short story using your words from the spelling word list.

2. Underline the spelling words in the story.

3. Correct any spelling errors.

Riddle Me This

1. Write a riddle for your words from the spelling word list.
   Example: "I have a trunk, but it's not on my car."

2. Write the answer, which is your word, for each riddle.
   Example: Answer: elephant

3. Correct any spelling errors.

RunOnWord

1. Gather some crayons, colored pencils, or markers. Write each of your words, using a different color for each word, end to end as one long word.
   Example: dogcatbirdfishturtle

2. Rewrite the words correctly and with proper spacing.

Complete the activity that you chose.

My chosen activity: _____

TRY IT
Who Is Sonia Sotomayor? (B)

Write About Facts and Opinions

Write your responses in the spaces provided.

1. Read each line from *Who Is Sonia Sotomayor?* Then write "F" under those that state facts, and write "O" under those that express opinions.

   "Morganthau was famous in New York. He was a tough prosecutor."

   _____

   "Finally, in 1992, Congress approved her. President George H.W. Bush named her as a federal judge."

   _____

   "So in 1984, she took a job at a law firm called Pavia & Harcourt."

   _____

   "Her office was tiny and unpleasant. It was usually too hot or too cold."

   _____

2. How could you verify the facts you identified in Question 1? What details might support the opinions you identified?

   _____
   _____
   _____
   _____

TRY IT

Who Is Sonia Sotomayor? (C)

Write About Sonia Sotomayor Using Text Features

Use the text features in *Who is Sonia Sotomayor?* to help you answer the questions. Write your responses in the spaces provided.

1. Turn to the table of contents. Why is the final chapter of the book called "One of Nine"?

   _____
   _____

2. Turn to page 98 of the book. How do the picture and caption on this page help readers better understand the text?

   _____
   _____

3. Why did author Megan Stine feel it was necessary to include the text box on pages 32 and 33?

   _____
   _____

4. Look at the time lines on pages 106 and 107.
   a. When was Sonia appointed a U.S. district court judge?
   b. When did the Major League Baseball strike begin?
   c. When did Sonia rule to help end the strike?

   _____

5. Turn to the bibliography on page 108. Which of the sources listed here would you be most interested in reading? Why? (Choose at least two.)

I can choose more than two, right?

TRY IT

Who Is Sonia Sotomayor? Wrap-Up

Write About *Who Is Sonia Sotomayor?*

Write your response in complete sentences.

Write a brief summary of *Who Is Sonia Sotomayor?* Your summary should

- Be at least three paragraphs long.
- Describe the most important figures and events in the text.
- Use chronological order.

TRY IT
Sonia Sotomayor's Opening Statement

Write About What You Learned

Use both Opening Statement to the Senate Judiciary Committee by Sonia Sotomayor and Megan Stine's *Who Is Sonia Sotomayor?* to answer the questions. Write your responses in the spaces provided.

1. What does the statement reveal about Sonia's father?

   _____

2. What does Stine's book reveal about Sonia's father?

   _____

3. According to the statement, what does Sonia believe she owes her success to?

   _____

4. According to Stine's book, how did Sonia succeed in high school, college, law school, and her professional life?

   _____

5. According to the statement, which case was Sonia best known for deciding as a district court judge?

   _____

6. According to Stine's book, which case was one of the biggest of Sonia's career when she was an assistant district attorney?

   _____

TRY IT

Sonia Sotomayor's Opening Statement Wrap-Up

Write About Sonia Sotomayor, Supreme Court Justice

Write your response in complete sentences.

Write about how Sonia Sotomayor became a Supreme Court justice. Your answer should

- Be two or three paragraphs long.
- Include your own descriptions of events, details, and people from both *Who Is Sonia Sotomayor?* and Opening Statement to Senate Judiciary Committee.
- Be structured in chronological order.

TRY IT
Logical Relationships

Write Sentences with Signal Words

For each word in this workshop, write one or two sentences that use the word correctly. The first one has been done for you.

1. however

   Sentence: I'll eat pizza hot or cold or however you want to serve it to me!

2. similarly

   _____
   _____

3. alternatively

   _____
   _____

4. additionally

   _____
   _____

5. nevertheless

   _____
   _____

6. although

_____
_____

7. moreover

_____
_____

GET READY

Opinion Writing: Prewriting (A)

Spelling List 19 Pretest

1. Open the Spelling Pretest activity online. Listen to the first spelling word. Type the word. Check your answer.

2. Write the correct spelling of the word in the Word column of the Spelling Pretest table on the next page.

	Word	✓	✗
1	blindfold		

3. Put a check mark in the ✓ column if you spelled the word correctly online.

	Word	✓	✗
1	blindfold	✓	

Put an X in the ✗ column if you spelled the word incorrectly online.

	Word	✓	✗
1	blindfold		X

4. Repeat Steps 1–3 for the remaining words in the Spelling Pretest.

Opinion Writing: Prewriting (A)

Spelling List 19 Pretest

Write each spelling word in the Word column, making sure to spell it correctly.

	Word	✓	✗
1			
2			
3			
4			
5			
6			
7			
8			
9			
10			
11			

	Word	✓	✗
12			
13			
14			
15			
16			
17			
18			
19			
20			
21			

TRY IT

Opinion Writing: Prewriting (A)

Brainstorm for Your Editorial

Read the writing assignment. You will complete the assignment in steps over multiple lessons.

Prompt: Write an editorial about an issue in your community.

Requirements: Your editorial should include the following:

- A **title**
- An **introduction** that gives necessary background information, states your opinion, and provides an organizational structure
- **Three logically ordered body paragraphs**, each centered on a reason for your opinion
- **Facts and details** that support each reason and address possible audience questions
- Information discovered during **research** and relevant **personal experience**
- **Transitions** that link your opinion and reasons, and your reasons and evidence
- A **conclusion** that restates your opinion in different words and includes a call to action for the audience
- Correct **grammar**, **usage**, and **mechanics**
- A list of at least three trustworthy **research sources**

Audience: You will identify an appropriate audience for your editorial based on your topic, opinion, and call to action.

Purpose: Convince your audience to support your call to action.

Length: 500 to 600 words long (2 to $2\frac{1}{2}$ typed, double-spaced pages)

Brainstorm and choose a topic for your editorial.

1. Think about your community. Think about the places, the rules, the traditions, the sports team, and more!

   a. List specific things you love about your community.

   b. List specific things you wish were different about your community.

OPINION WRITING: PREWRITING (A)

2. Read your answers to Question 1.

   a. Circle the two topics that you listed that most interest you.

   b. For each topic you chose, try stating an opinion and a call to action. Two examples have been provided.

Topic: I love that my town has a food pantry.

Opinion: Donating food to the town food pantry is important.

Call to Action: At least once a month, donate food to the food pantry.

Topic: I dislike that there isn't a stop sign at the intersection near my house.

Opinion: The intersection of Oak Leather Dr. and Burnside Landing Dr. needs a stop sign.

Call to Action: Support me when I speak at the next town hall meeting.

Topic 1:
_____
_____

Opinion:
_____
_____

Call to Action:
_____
_____

OPINION WRITING: PREWRITING (A)

Topic 2:
_____
_____

Opinion:
_____
_____

Call to Action:
_____
_____

3. Decide which of the opinions you wrote in Question 2 interests you more. Then answer Yes or No to each question.

   a. Is your opinion focused enough to cover in detail in five paragraphs? _____

   b. Is your opinion something you can support with at least three reasons? _____

   c. Is there a realistic call to action related to your opinion? _____

4. Did you answer Yes to Parts A–C of Question 3? If so, you have found your editorial topic! If not, go back to the topics you listed in Question 1, choose a different topic, and follow the process described in Questions 2 and 3.

   The opinion that I am going to support in my editorial is
   _____
   _____.

GET READY

Opinion Writing: Prewriting (B)

Spelling List 19 Activity Bank

Circle any words in the box that you did not spell correctly on the pretest. Using your circled words, complete one activity of your choice. Complete as much of the activity as you can in the time given.

If you spelled all words correctly on the pretest, complete your chosen activity with as many spelling words as you can.

changeable	admirable	admissible	reversible	barbarism
knowledgeable	debatable	permissible	grateful	hypnotism
manageable	inescapable	invincible	gratify	patriotism
noticeable	mistakable	responsible	gratitude	tourism
replaceable				

Spelling Activity Choices

Hidden Words

1. Draw a picture and "hide" as many words from the Spelling Word List inside the picture as you can.
2. See if others can find the words within the picture.

Triangle Spelling

Write each word in a triangle.

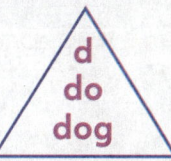

Ghost Words

1. Use a white crayon to write each spelling word.
2. Go over the white crayon writing with a colored marker

Complete the activity that you chose.

My chosen activity: _____

TRY IT

Opinion Writing: Prewriting (B)

Research Your Editorial

Follow these steps to write research questions.

1. Write the opinion that you are going to support in your editorial.
   Sample Opinion: Donating food to the town food pantry is important.
   My Opinion:
   _____
   _____

2. List at least three reasons that you have for your opinion. Write questions that you can research to support each reason.

Reasons	Research Questions
Sample: Everyone deserves to have enough to eat.	**Sample:** What are the effects of not having enough to eat?

Follow these steps to conduct research. Record information on the Research Notes pages that follow. Use one page per source.

3. Identify at least three sources (digital, print, or both) that you can use to answer your research questions. Record the title, author, publisher, and URL of each source.

4. As you read each source, take notes related to your research questions.
   - Write your notes in your own words.
   - If you find a direct quotation that you think you might use in your editorial, record the quotation, word for word, in quotation marks. Also record the name of the person you are quoting.

Research can uncover surprises. You can adjust your research questions!

Research Notes

Source

Title: _____

Author: _____

Published by: _____

URL (if necessary): _____

Notes

Key Information Written in Your Own Words:

_____

_____

_____

_____

_____

_____

Direct Quotation:

_____

_____

_____

Person Quoted: _____

Research Notes

Source

Title: _____

Author: _____

Published by: _____

URL (if necessary): _____

Notes

Key Information Written in Your Own Words:

_____

_____

_____

_____

_____

Direct Quotation:

_____

_____

_____

Person Quoted: _____

TRY IT

Opinion Writing: Prewriting (C)

Plan Your Editorial

Review your research notes. Then complete the graphic organizer to plan your editorial. You do not need to use complete sentences.

- Top section: State your opinion.

- Middle sections: State your three supporting reasons. For each reason, list supporting facts and details you discovered during your research. Also, list any supporting personal experience.

- Bottom section: Restate your opinion, and state your call to action (what you want the audience to do).

Title: _____

Opinion:
_____
_____
_____

Reason 1:
_____

Evidence

Research: _____

_____

_____

Personal Experience: _____

_____

_____

Reason 2:
_____

Evidence

Research: _____

_____

_____

Personal Experience: _____

_____

_____

Reason 3:
_____

Evidence

Research: _____
_____
_____
_____

Personal Experience: _____
_____
_____

Opinion, Reworded:
_____
_____

Call to Action:
_____
_____

TRY IT

Opinion Writing: Drafting (A)

Draft Your Editorial

Using your notes and your graphic organizer to guide you, write the first draft of your editorial. Write only on the white rows. You will use the purple rows for revisions later.

Note: List your sources at the end of your draft. For each source, include the title, author, publisher, and URL.

Title _____

start here ▶

keep writing ▶

Draft Page 1

keep writing ▶

Draft Page 2

Draft Page 3

keep writing ▶

keep writing ▶

Draft Page 5

Draft Page 6

TRY IT
Homonyms and Homographs

Apply: Homonyms and Homographs

Read the given word and sentence. Write a sentence using a homophone or homograph of the given word. The first one has been done for you.

1. Word: **bow**

   Sentence: The little girl has a pink **bow** in her hair.

   The audience clapped as the actor took a **bow**.

2. Word: **duck**

   Sentence: The mother **duck** walked her ducklings to the pond.

   _____
   _____

3. Word: **wind**

   Sentence: The **wind** was so strong it blew his hat off his head.

   _____
   _____

4. Word: **pool**

   Sentence: On a hot day, it is refreshing to jump into a **pool**.

   _____
   _____

5. Word: **lead**

   Sentence: The owner will **lead** the horse to the water.

   _____

   _____

6. Word: **point**

   Sentence: **Point** to the letter A on the page.

   _____

   _____

Did that bat just bat its eyes at me?

GET READY

Inside Out and Back Again (A)

Spelling List 20 Pretest

1. Open the Spelling Pretest activity online. Listen to the first spelling word. Type the word. Check your answer.

2. Write the correct spelling of the word in the Word column of the Spelling Pretest table on the next page.

	Word	✓	✗
1	blindfold		

3. Put a check mark in the ✓ column if you spelled the word correctly online.

   Put an X in the ✗ column if you spelled the word incorrectly online.

	Word	✓	✗
1	blindfold	✓	

	Word	✓	✗
1	blindfold		X

4. Repeat Steps 1–3 for the remaining words in the Spelling Pretest.

INSIDE OUT AND BACK AGAIN (A)

Inside Out and Back Again (A)

Spelling List 20 Pretest

Write each spelling word in the Word column, making sure to spell it correctly.

	Word	✓	✗
1			
2			
3			
4			
5			
6			
7			
8			
9			

	Word	✓	✗
10			
11			
12			
13			
14			
15			
16			
17			

TRY IT
Inside Out and Back Again (A)

Write About Visual Elements in Poetry

Read this excerpt from *Inside Out and Back Again* by Thanhha Lai.

Two More Papayas

I see them first.

Two green thumbs
that will grow into
orange-yellow delights
smelling of summer.

Middle sweet
between a mango and a pear.

Soft as a yam
gliding down
after three easy,
thrilling chews.

Think about the meaning of the excerpt.

a. List at least two visual elements that the author uses.

___

b. Explain how those elements support the meaning of the excerpt.

___

GET READY

Inside Out and Back Again (B)

Spelling List 20 Activity Bank

Circle any words in the box that you did not spell correctly on the pretest. Using your circled words, complete one activity of your choice. Complete as much of the activity as you can in the time given.

If you spelled all words correctly on the pretest, complete your chosen activity with as many spelling words as you can.

addiction	projection	rejection	appreciation	initial
attraction	deduction	celebration	motivation	initiate
conviction	contraction	protection	regulation	initiative
correction	reaction			

Spelling Activity Choices

Create a Crossword

1. Write a word from your spelling word list in the center of the grid paper.

2. Write another spelling word going across and sharing a letter with the first word. See how many words you can connect.

   Example:

			p			
		k	i	s	s	e	s
	d		n			
r	o	c	k	s		
	g					
	s					

Word Search Puzzle

1. Draw a box on the grid paper. The box should be large enough to hold your words from the spelling word list.

2. Fill in the grid paper with words from your spelling list, writing them horizontally, vertically, and diagonally (forward and backward if you choose).

3. Fill in the rest of the box with random letters.

4. Ask someone to find and circle your spelling words in the puzzle you made.

Complete the activity that you chose.

My chosen activity: _____

TRY IT

Inside out and Back Again (B)

Making a Prediction

Before you read pages 32–69 of *Inside Out and Back Again*, make a prediction about what you will read. Write your response to the first item in the spaces provided. After you have finished reading pages 32–69, come back and complete the second item.

1. Before you read pages 32–69, predict what will happen next for Há and her family.

   _____
   _____
   _____
   _____
   _____
   _____
   _____
   _____
   _____
   _____
   _____

2. Now that you have finished reading pages 32–69, confirm or modify your prediction using evidence from the text.

TRY IT
Inside Out and Back Again (C)

Special Delivery

Write your response in the space provided.

When Hà and her family first arrive on Guam, life in the tent city is both dull and frightening. That is because there is very little to do all day and because as refugees they face an uncertain future.

What happens to lift the spirits of Hà and the other Vietnamese people living on Guam? Describe how the events before and after this change are connected. Then briefly tell about a time when you found yourself cheered by a surprise and how it relates to this moment in the novel.

_____
_____
_____
_____
_____
_____
_____
_____
_____
_____
_____
_____

It was a surprise when I woke up to a foot of snow... in April!

TRY IT

Inside Out and Back Again (D)

Theme and Character Response

One theme of *Inside Out and Back Again* is that in difficult times, family members help and support each other.

Think about Hà's mother and how she responds to the challenges the family faces.

a. What is one piece of textual evidence that shows how Hà's mother responds to a challenge?

_____
_____
_____
_____
_____
_____

b. Explain how your evidence in Part A supports the given theme.

_____
_____
_____
_____
_____
_____

GET READY

Inside Out and Back Again (E)

Spelling List 21 Pretest

1. Open the Spelling Pretest activity online. Listen to the first spelling word. Type the word. Check your answer.

2. Write the correct spelling of the word in the Word column of the Spelling Pretest table on the next page.

	Word	✓	✗
1	blindfold		

3. Put a check mark in the ✓ column if you spelled the word correctly online.

	Word	✓	✗
1	blindfold	✓	

Put an X in the ✗ column if you spelled the word incorrectly online.

	Word	✓	✗
1	blindfold		X

4. Repeat Steps 1–3 for the remaining words in the Spelling Pretest.

Inside Out and Back Again (E)

Spelling List 21 Pretest

Write each spelling word in the Word column, making sure to spell it correctly.

#	Word	✓	✗
1			
2			
3			
4			
5			
6			
7			
8			
9			
10			
11			

#	Word	✓	✗
12			
13			
14			
15			
16			
17			
18			
19			
20			
21			

TRY IT

Inside Out and Back Again (E)

Identify Figurative Language

Read the phrase. Then read the excerpt from *Inside Out and Back Again* in which the phrase is used.

Identify which type of figurative language the phrase is an example of: *alliteration, metaphor, onomatopoeia,* or *simile.*

1. Phrase: ***like a caged puppy***

   Excerpt:

   But
   he looks
   more defeated than weak,
   more helpless than scared,
   like a caged puppy. (p. 226)

   Type of figurative language: _____

2. Phrase: ***hush, hush***

   Excerpt:

   Hush, hush,
   hush, hush.
   She says it over and over,
   like a chant,
   slowly. (p. 210)

   Type of figurative language: _____

3. Phrase: ***misery keeps pouncing on me***

   Excerpt:

   It's time to tell Mother

   why *misery*

   keeps pouncing on me. (p. 213)

   Type of figurative language: _____

4. Phrase: ***cool to a real whisper***

   Excerpt:

   Slowly

   the screams that never stopped

   inside my head

   cool to a real whisper. (p. 210)

   Type of figurative language: _____

5. Phrase: ***drops from wet hair drip down***

   Excerpt:

   Drops from wet hair

   drip down my back. (p. 172)

   Type of figurative language: _____

6. Phrase: ***clink clank***

   Excerpt:

   I hear the clink clank

   of Brother Khôi's bicycle (p. 154)

   Type of figurative language: _____

GET READY

Inside Out and Back Again (F)

Spelling List 21 Activity Bank

Circle any words in the box that you did not spell correctly on the pretest. Using your circled words, complete one activity of your choice. Complete as much of the activity as you can in the time given.

If you spelled all words correctly on the pretest, complete your chosen activity with as many spelling words as you can.

coarse	heel	poll	border	rite
course	loan	pore	review	wright
flea	lone	pour	revue	foul
flee	pole	boarder	right	fowl
heal				

Spelling Activity Choices

Vowel-Free Words

1. In the left column, write only the consonants in each word and put a dot where each vowel should be.

2. Spell each word out loud, stating which vowels should be in the places you wrote dots.

3. In the right column, rewrite the entire spelling word.

4. Correct any spelling errors.

Alphabetizing

1. In the left column, write your words from the spelling word list in alphabetical order.

2. Correct any spelling errors.

Parts of Speech

1. In the left column, write the words from your spelling list that are nouns.

2. In the right column, write all the other words from your spelling list and label each word's part of speech.

3. Correct any spelling errors.

Uppercase and Lowercase

1. In the left column, write each of your words in all capital (uppercase) letters.

2. In the right column, write each of your words in all lowercase letters.

3. Correct any spelling errors.

Complete the activity that you chose.

My chosen activity: _____

1. _____   _____
2. _____   _____
3. _____   _____
4. _____   _____
5. _____   _____
6. _____   _____
7. _____   _____
8. _____   _____
9. _____   _____
10. _____   _____
11. _____   _____
12. _____   _____
13. _____   _____
14. _____   _____
15. _____   _____
16. _____   _____
17. _____   _____
18. _____   _____
19. _____   _____
20. _____   _____
21. _____   _____
22. _____   _____
23. _____   _____
24. _____   _____
25. _____   _____

TRY IT

Inside Out and Back Again (F)

Plan a Narrative Poem

Use the prompt to answer the questions.

Prompt: Write a short narrative poem in the style of *Inside Out and Back Again*.

1. Choose a topic for your poem.

   a. Brainstorm small moments from your life that were meaningful to you, such as the first day in a new place, a special holiday celebration, or a day you faced a challenge.

   Brainstorm

   b. Circle the moment that you would like to write about in your poem.

2. List characteristics about the speaker: you! Your narrative poem will be told in first person. If you wish, you can draw a picture to help you plan.

   Speaker (you)

3. List details about the setting. Use concrete and sensory language. You don't need to write complete sentences. Include at least three of the five senses. If you wish, you can draw a picture to help you plan.

Setting

4. List three feelings the speaker (you) has during the events in the narrative. Write either a short description or a short dialogue that shows each feeling.

Feeling	Description or Dialogue

5. Describe the beginning, middle, and end of your narrative poem. Use details from your answers to Questions 2–4. You do not need to use complete sentences.

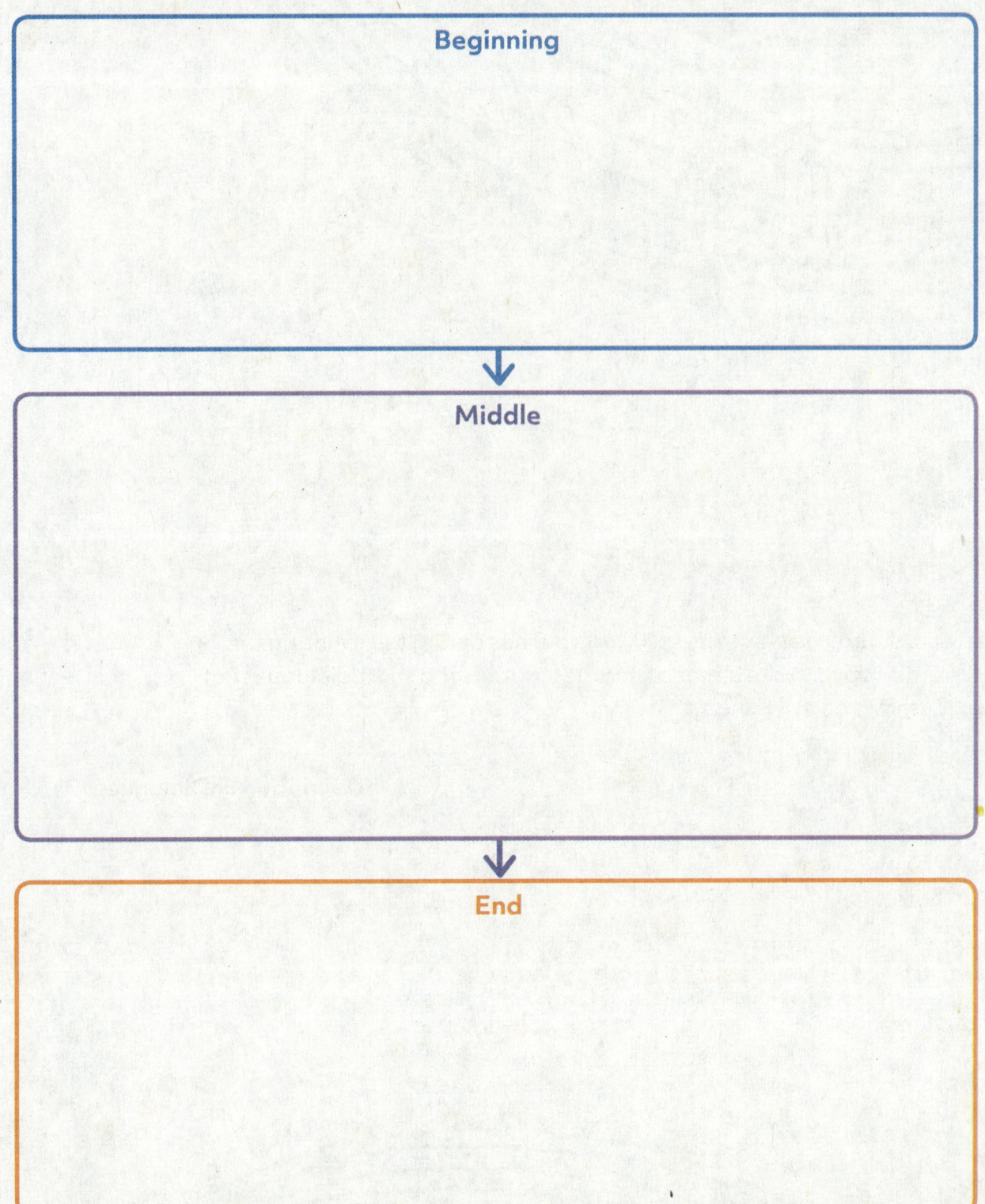

INSIDE OUT AND BACK AGAIN (F)

TRY IT
Inside Out and Back Again (G)

Write a Narrative Poem

Write the first draft of your narrative poem. Write only on the white rows. You will use the purple rows for revisions later.

Prompt: Write a short narrative poem in the style of *Inside Out and Back Again*.

As you write, use the following elements of narrative poetry: dialogue, imagery, figurative language, purposeful line breaks, and stanza breaks.

Title _____

start here ▶

keep writing ▶

Draft Page 1

Draft Page 2

Draft Page 4

TRY IT

Inside Out and Back Again (H)

Revise and Publish a Narrative Poem

Read your poem. Then use the checklist to revise your poem, using the purple lines to make changes.

Organization

☐ Does my poem have a clear beginning, middle, and end?

☐ Is my poem written in sequential order?

Content

☐ Are the speaker and setting clearly described?

☐ Have I used figurative language or imagery to show, not tell?

☐ Does my poem have dialogue to show feelings?

☐ Have I used precise language throughout the poem?

TRY IT

Inside Out and Back Again Wrap-Up

Summary of Inside Out and Back Again

Write your response in complete sentences.

Write a summary of *Inside Out and Back Again*. Write your ideas in sequential order, and include only the main characters, events, and key details.

TRY IT

Opinion Writing: Revising

Revise Your Editorial

Use the checklist as you revise the draft of your editorial.

Organization

☐ Does my editorial have an introduction, at least three body paragraphs, and a conclusion?

☐ Does my introduction state the reasons for my opinion in the order they are presented in the body paragraphs?

☐ Are my body paragraphs in a logical order?

☐ Does each paragraph begin with a topic sentence?

☐ Are supporting facts and details grouped in the correct body paragraphs?

☐ Do I use clear and logical transitions?

Content

☐ Does my introduction clearly state my opinion and include background information about my topic?

☐ Does each body paragraph focus on a reason that supports my opinion?

☐ Do I use enough facts and details, including at least one personal experience, to support each reason?

- [ ] Is my editorial factual and well researched?
- [ ] Are the words I use precise and domain-specific?
- [ ] Does my conclusion restate my opinion and reasons, using different words? Does it include a call to action for the audience?
- [ ] Do I have a list of at least three trustworthy research sources?

To revise, I use scissors to cut out each paragraph. Then I rearrange them!

TRY IT

Opinion Writing: Proofreading

Proofread Your Editorial

Use the checklist as you proofread your revised draft of your editorial.

Grammar and Usage

- [ ] Are all sentences complete and correct?
- [ ] Are there any missing or extra words?
- [ ] Are all verbs in the appropriate tense?
- [ ] Are there other grammatical or usage errors?

Mechanics

- [ ] Is every word spelled correctly, including frequently confused words?
- [ ] Does every sentence begin with a capital letter and end with the appropriate punctuation?
- [ ] Are commas used correctly to set off tag questions, direct addresses, and the words *yes* and *no*?
- [ ] Are commas used correctly in series of items and to set off introductory elements?
- [ ] Is punctuation used thoughtfully and effectively?

- [ ] Are the titles of works in the source list capitalized and formatted correctly?

- [ ] Are direct quotations punctuated correctly?

- [ ] Are there other punctuation or capitalization errors?

GET READY
Choice Reading Project

Spelling List 22 Pretest

1. Open the Spelling Pretest activity online. Listen to the first spelling word. Type the word. Check your answer.

2. Write the correct spelling of the word in the Word column of the Spelling Pretest table on the next page.

	Word	✓	✗
1	blindfold		

3. Put a check mark in the ✓ column if you spelled the word correctly online.

	Word	✓	✗
1	blindfold	✓	

Put an X in the ✗ column if you spelled the word incorrectly online.

	Word	✓	✗
1	blindfold		X

4. Repeat Steps 1–3 for the remaining words in the Spelling Pretest.

Choice Reading Project

Spelling List 22 Pretest

Write each spelling word in the Word column, making sure to spell it correctly.

#	Word	✓	✗
1			
2			
3			
4			
5			
6			
7			
8			
9			

#	Word	✓	✗
10			
11			
12			
13			
14			
15			
16			
17			

GET READY
Choice Reading Project

Spelling List 22 Activity Bank

Circle any words in the box that you did not spell correctly on the pretest. Using your circled words, complete one activity of your choice. Complete as much of the activity as you can in the time given.

If you spelled all words correctly on the pretest, complete your chosen activity with as many spelling words as you can.

cycle	muscular	popular	public	signature
cyclic	pleasant	popularity	publicity	design
cyclist	please	population	sign	designation
muscle	pleasure			

Spelling Activity Choices

Silly Sentences

1. Write a silly sentence using your words from the spelling word list.
2. Underline the spelling word in each sentence.
   Example: The dog was <u>driving</u> a car.
3. Correct any spelling errors.

Spelling Story

1. Write a very short story using your words from the spelling word list.

2. Underline the spelling words in the story.

3. Correct any spelling errors.

Riddle Me This

1. Write a riddle for your words from the spelling word list.
   Example: "I have a trunk, but it's not on my car."

2. Write the answer, which is your word, for each riddle.
   Example: Answer: elephant

3. Correct any spelling errors.

RunOnWord

1. Gather some crayons, colored pencils, or markers. Write each of your words, using a different color for each word, end to end as one long word.
   Example: dogcatbirdfishturtle

2. Rewrite the words correctly and with proper spacing.

Complete the activity that you chose.

My chosen activity: _____

GET READY
Choice Reading Project

Spelling List 23 Pretest

1. Open the Spelling Pretest activity online. Listen to the first spelling word. Type the word. Check your answer.

2. Write the correct spelling of the word in the Word column of the Spelling Pretest table on the next page.

	Word	✓	✗
1	blindfold		

3. Put a check mark in the ✓ column if you spelled the word correctly online.

	Word	✓	✗
1	blindfold	✓	

Put an X in the ✗ column if you spelled the word incorrectly online.

	Word	✓	✗
1	blindfold		✗

4. Repeat Steps 1–3 for the remaining words in the Spelling Pretest.

Choice Reading Project

Spelling List 23 Pretest

Write each spelling word in the Word column, making sure to spell it correctly.

	Word	✓	✗
1			
2			
3			
4			
5			
6			
7			
8			
9			

	Word	✓	✗
10			
11			
12			
13			
14			
15			
16			
17			

GET READY
Choice Reading Project

Spelling List 23 Activity Bank

Circle any words in the box that you did not spell correctly on the pretest. Using your circled words, complete one activity of your choice. Complete as much of the activity as you can in the time given.

If you spelled all words correctly on the pretest, complete your chosen activity with as many spelling words as you can.

billfold	grandparent	newscast	scarecrow	minimum
clothesline	sideways	outstanding	whoever	miniature
copyright	household	peppermint	worthwhile	minus
gentleman	motorcycle			

Spelling Activity Choices

Hidden Words

1. Draw a picture and "hide" as many words from the Spelling Word List as they can inside the picture.
2. See if others can find the words within the picture.

Triangle Spelling

Write each word in a triangle.

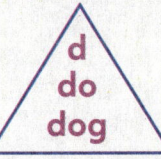

Ghost Words

1. Use a white crayon to write each spelling word.
2. Go over the white crayon writing with a colored marker.

Complete the activity that you chose.

My chosen activity: _____

TRY IT

Presentation Skills (A)

Present Your Opinion

Use the prompt to answer the questions.

Prompt: Give an opinion speech that is approximately one minute long. Choose a topic that you do not need to research.

1. Write notes about what you will say in your speech.

> **Beginning: Say what you're going to say.**
>
> **My opinion:**
>
> **My three reasons:**
>
> ....
>
> **Middle: Say it!**
>
> **Reason 1:**
>
> Facts and descriptive details:
>
> **Reason 2:**
>
> Facts and descriptive details:
>
> **Reason 3:**
>
> Facts and descriptive details:
>
> ....
>
> **End: Say what you said.**
>
> **My opinion and reasons restated:**
>
> **Final thoughts:**

2. Record your speech.
   - Refer to your graphic organizer from Question 1 as you speak.
   - Speak clearly, distinctly, and at an understandable pace.

3. Listen to your speech. Then answer these questions.
   a. Were your ideas well organized? Why or why not?

   _____
   _____

   b. Which details were most descriptive? Which details could be more descriptive?

   _____
   _____

   c. Were any details not relevant to your opinion? If so, which ones?

   _____
   _____

   d. Did you speak too quickly or too slowly during any parts of your speech? Identify one way you could improve your pace.

   _____
   _____

   e. Did you speak all words clearly and distinctly? Identify one way you could improve your speaking.

   _____
   _____

TRY IT

Presentation Skills (B)

Add Pictures to Your Opinion Speech

Use the prompt to answer the questions.

Prompt: Give an opinion speech that is approximately one minute long. Choose a topic that you do not need to research.

1. Think about a visual—such as a picture, diagram, map, or video clip—that would enhance your opinion speech.

    a. Describe, draw, or paste a copy of the visual.

b. At what part of your speech would it make sense to show your visual? For example, would you show it at the beginning? During Reason 1?

_____

c. How does the visual support your opinion? Explain.

_____
_____
_____

2. Read your answers to Question 3 of the Present Your Opinion activity page. List at least three ways you can improve your speech.

_____
_____
_____
_____

3. Deliver your speech to your Learning Coach.
   - Include the improvements you described in Question 2.
   - Display the visual you described in Question 1 (if possible) at the most logical point for it in your speech.

TRY IT

Presentation Skills Wrap-Up

Use Presentation Skills

Use the prompt to answer the questions.

Prompt: Which school subject is the most valuable for students? To answer the question, give a speech that is approximately one minute long.

1. Write notes about what you will say in your speech.

> **Beginning: Say what you're going to say.**
>
> **My opinion:**
>
> **My three reasons:**
>
> ··
>
> **Middle: Say it!**
>
> **Reason 1:**
>
> Facts and descriptive details:
>
> **Reason 2:**
>
> Facts and descriptive details:
>
> **Reason 3:**
>
> Facts and descriptive details:
>
> ··
>
> **End: Say what you said.**
>
> **My opinion and reasons restated:**
>
> **Final thoughts:**

PRESENTATION SKILLS WRAP-UP

2. Think about a visual—such as a picture, diagram, map, or video clip—that would enhance your opinion speech.

   a. Describe, draw, or paste a copy of the visual.

   b. At what point in your speech would it make sense to show your visual? For example, would you show it at the beginning? During Reason 1?

   _____
   _____

3. Record your speech.
   - Refer to your graphic organizer from Question 1 as you speak.
   - Speak clearly, distinctly, and at an understandable pace.
   - Display the visual that you described in Question 1 (if possible) at the most logical point for it in your speech.

4. Listen to your speech.

   a. Describe two strengths of your speech.

   _____
   _____
   _____
   _____

   b. Describe two ways you could improve your speech.

   _____
   _____
   _____
   _____

PRESENTATION SKILLS WRAP-UP

TRY IT

Idioms

Apply: Idioms

An idiom is a group of words that does not actually mean what it says. For example, *raining cats and dogs* does not mean cats and dogs are falling from the sky. It means it is raining very hard outside.

Read each sentence. Use the context clues in the sentence to help you define the idiom. In the box, draw the idiom.

1. Sentence: Every time I play in the annual piano recital, I **get cold feet**. My palms get sweaty and my heart beats fast.

    Idiom: **get cold feet**

    Define:

    _____

    Draw

IDIOMS **401**

2. Sentence: You are in such a bad mood today. Did you **wake up on the wrong side of the bed?**

   Idiom: **wake up on the wrong side of the bed**

   Define:

   _____

   Draw

3. Sentence: I have had it with my little brother's whining! I am **at the end of my rope**!

   Idiom: **at the end of my rope**

   Define:

   _____

   Draw

GET READY
"From Barter to Bitcoin"

Spelling List 24 Pretest

1. Open the Spelling Pretest activity online. Listen to the first spelling word. Type the word. Check your answer.

2. Write the correct spelling of the word in the Word column of the Spelling Pretest table on the next page.

	Word	✓	✗
1	blindfold		

3. Put a check mark in the ✓ column if you spelled the word correctly online.

	Word	✓	✗
1	blindfold	✓	

Put an X in the ✗ column if you spelled the word incorrectly online.

	Word	✓	✗
1	blindfold		X

4. Repeat Steps 1–3 for the remaining words in the Spelling Pretest.

"From Barter to Bitcoin"

Spelling List 24 Pretest

Write each spelling word in the Word column, making sure to spell it correctly.

#	Word	✓	✗
1			
2			
3			
4			
5			
6			
7			
8			
9			

#	Word	✓	✗
10			
11			
12			
13			
14			
15			
16			
17			

TRY IT

"From Barter to Bitcoin"

Write About Two Ways of Buying Goods

Respond in complete sentences.

Based on "From Barter to Bitcoin," explain how bartering and bitcoin are related. How did people go from one to the other over time? How are they similar? How are they different?

_____
_____
_____
_____
_____
_____
_____
_____
_____

I need to think about this for a bit.

GET READY

"From Barter to Bitcoin" Wrap-Up

Spelling List 24 Activity Bank

Circle any words in the box that you did not spell correctly on the pretest. Using your circled words, complete one activity of your choice. Complete as much of the activity as you can in the time given.

If you spelled all words correctly on the pretest, complete your chosen activity with as many spelling words as you can.

capital	patience	profit	stationery	flammable
capitol	patients	prophet	weather	flame
dual	principal	stationary	whether	inflammation
duel	principle			

Spelling Activity Choices

Create a Crossword

1. Write a word from your spelling word list in the center of the grid paper.

2. Write another spelling word going across and sharing a letter with the first word. See how many words you can connect.

   Example:

			p			
		k	i	s	s	e	s
	d		n			
r	o	c	k	s		
	g					
	s					

Word Search Puzzle

1. Draw a box on the grid paper. The box should be large enough to hold your words from the spelling word list.

2. Fill in the grid paper with words from your spelling list, writing them horizontally, vertically, and diagonally (forward and backward if you choose).

3. Fill in the rest of the box with random letters.

4. Ask someone to find and circle your spelling words in the puzzle you made.

Complete the activity that you chose.

My chosen activity: _____

TRY IT

"From Barter to Bitcoin" Wrap-Up

Write About "From Barter to Bitcoin"

Respond in complete sentences.

How does the structure of "From Barter to Bitcoin" affect your understanding of the ideas expressed in the text? Use details from the text in your response.

_____
_____
_____
_____
_____
_____
_____
_____

TRY IT
"Making Money"

Write About a Process

Respond in complete sentences.

How does each step in the coin-making process help create a strong finished product? Which steps ensure that coins have the correct size, weight, texture, shape, strength, and appearance?

_____
_____
_____
_____
_____
_____
_____
_____
_____
_____

TRY IT

"Making Money" Wrap-Up

Write About "Making Money"

Respond in complete sentences.

How does the structure of "Making Money" affect your understanding of the text? How might this article be different with a different structure? Use examples from the text in your answer.

_____
_____
_____
_____
_____
_____
_____
_____

Good writers think about which structure is best for their purpose.

TRY IT

Economy Words

Apply: Using Context Clues

Read the passage. Use context clues in the sentences to determine the meaning of the words about the economy.

Everyday people use **currency**, or money, to buy something. But how do people earn money? To earn money, people need to work to earn an **income**. It is a good idea to deposit as much as you can. That helps build your **credit** at the bank. You can always **withdraw** money from your account as you need it. However, when you withdraw money, make sure to take out only the money you have planned for within your **budget**. For example, if you plan to spend $50 at the grocery store, then stick to your budget and only withdraw $50.

Sometimes, for very large purchases like a car or a house, people may take out a **loan** from a bank. However, this loan will come at an extra cost, so you need to consider this carefully. It is important to make sure the loan you ask for is an amount of money you can pay back in a certain amount of time. If you are unable to, then you will have a **debt** to pay off. This could quickly amount to too much money if you are not careful!

Use context clues to create your definition of the words about the economy. Record your answers in the table.

Word	Your Definition
currency	
income	
credit	
withdraw	
budget	
loan	
debt	

418 ECONOMY WORDS

GET READY

Presentation: Digital Tools

Spelling List 25 Pretest

1. Open the Spelling Pretest activity online. Listen to the first spelling word. Type the word. Check your answer.

2. Write the correct spelling of the word in the Word column of the Spelling Pretest table on the next page.

3. Put a check mark in the ✓ column if you spelled the word correctly online.

   Put an X in the ✗ column if you spelled the word incorrectly online.

4. Repeat Steps 1–3 for the remaining words in the Spelling Pretest.

PRESENTATION: DIGITAL TOOLS 419

Presentation: Digital Tools

Spelling List 25 Pretest

Write each spelling word in the Word column, making sure to spell it correctly.

#	Word	✓	✗
1			
2			
3			
4			
5			
6			
7			
8			
9			
10			
11			

#	Word	✓	✗
12			
13			
14			
15			
16			
17			
18			
19			
20			
21			

TRY IT

Presentation: Digital Tools

Use Presentation Software

Use presentation software to complete this activity.

1. Open the presentation software and select **Blank Presentation**.

2. Go to **File > Save As**, and select a location on your computer in which to save your presentation. Give your presentation a name. Do not delete the file extension (for example, ".pptx") from your name.

3. Create the slides of your presentation.

   a. **Slide 1:** Add a title and a subtitle to the first slide of your presentation. The title and subtitle can be anything you like. For example, a title could be "Rescue Dogs," and a subtitle could be "Powerful Potential Pets."

   b. **Slide 2:** Select **New Slide** from the Home tab to create a second slide. Add a title and at least two bullets with text next to them to your slide. Your bullets should relate to your title.

   c. **Slide 3:** Select **New Slide** to create a third slide. Add a title to your slide. Then add a picture by selecting the Pictures icon on the slide or by going to **Insert > Pictures**. Select a picture that is on your computer (for example, a picture from the Sample Pictures folder). If you can't find a picture that relates to your title, that's okay. Finally, select **Insert > Text Box** and create a narrow text box below your picture. Inside the text box, add a short caption that describes your picture.

   d. **Slide 4:** Select **New Slide** to create a fourth slide. Add a title to your slide. Then go to **Insert > Audio > Record Audio**. Press the record button (a red circle), and talk for about 30 seconds. When you have finished recording, press the stop button (a blue square). Then press OK. Move the speaker icon to the lower left-hand corner of the slide. If you wish, add bullets and text to the slide.

4. Reorder Slides 2 and 3. To do this, drag Slide 2 below Slide 3 in the left-hand viewing pane.

5. Select **Slide Show > From Beginning**. Review your presentation!

6. Save your presentation to your computer using **File > Save** or the Save icon.

GET READY

Presentation: Planning

Spelling List 25 Activity Bank

Circle any words in the box that you did not spell correctly on the pretest. Using your circled words, complete one activity of your choice. Complete as much of the activity as you can in the time given.

If you spelled all words correctly on the pretest, complete your chosen activity with as many spelling words as you can.

addition	composition	intrusion	transportation	irrational
clarification	conclusion	multiplication	novel	irregular
collision	exclamation	qualification	novelty	irresponsible
combination	extension	relaxation	renovate	irreplaceable
competition				

Spelling Activity Choices

Silly Sentences

1. Write a silly sentence using your words from the spelling word list.

2. Underline the spelling word in each sentence.
   Example: The dog was driving a car.

3. Correct any spelling errors.

PRESENTATION: PLANNING **423**

Spelling Story

1. Write a very short story using your words from the spelling word list.

2. Underline the spelling words in the story.

3. Correct any spelling errors.

Riddle Me This

1. Write a riddle for your words from the spelling word list.
   Example: "I have a trunk, but it's not on my car."

2. Write the answer, which is your word, for each riddle.
   Example: Answer: elephant

3. Correct any spelling errors.

RunOnWord

1. Gather some crayons, colored pencils, or markers. Write each of your words, using a different color for each word, end to end as one long word.
   Example: dogcatbirdfishturtle

2. Rewrite the words correctly and with proper spacing.

- **Complete the activity that you chose.**

  My chosen activity: _____

PRESENTATION: PLANNING

TRY IT

Presentation: Planning

Plan Your Presentation

Read the assignment. You will complete the assignment in steps over multiple lessons.

Prompt: Use presentation software to create an informational presentation about a historical figure.

Requirements:
Every slide except for the title and source slides should include a heading, bulleted talking points, media, and audio of you speaking. Use the template provided to create the following slides:

- A **title slide**

- An **introduction** slide that catches the audience's attention, states the main idea, and briefly states the supporting ideas in the order you will present them

- At least four **body** slides, each organized around a supporting idea that is developed with facts and descriptive details. The body slides should provide the following information, organized as you feel is most effective:
  - Where was the person born? What was the person's childhood like?
  - What was the person's main accomplishment? What did that person do to achieve that accomplishment?
  - What events affected the person's life and accomplishments? Did he or she face any obstacles? Did he or she make any mistakes?
  - What is the person's legacy, or influence on life today?
  - What are some fun facts about the person or quotes the person said?

- A **conclusion** slide that restates your main idea

- A **sources** slide that lists at least three trustworthy research sources

Be sure to do the following:

- Speak clearly and at an appropriate pace.
- Include relevant information from your research and your personal experience.
- Include the **URLs** of any media used in the presentation that you found online.
- Use correct **grammar**, **usage**, and **mechanics**.

Audience: Your teacher and peers

Purpose: Inform your audience about your historical figure.

Brainstorm and choose a topic for your presentation.

1. Think about people from history (living or dead) whom you have enjoyed learning about. These people may inspire you or simply fascinate you. List as many people as you can think of.

2. Read your answers to Question 1.

   a. Choose two people that interest you the most.

   b. For each person you chose, do a quick Internet search and read a little bit about that person.

3. Decide which person you chose in Question 2 interests you more. Then answer Yes or No to each question.

   a. Is this person someone I can learn about through research?

   _____

   b. Am I excited to spend a lot of time learning about this person?

   _____

4. Did you answer Yes to Parts A and B of Question 3? You have found your presentation topic! If not, go back to the topics you listed in Question 1, choose a different topic, and follow the process described in Questions 2 and 3.

   My presentation will be about this historical figure:

   _____

TRY IT

Presentation: Research

Research Your Presentation

Follow these steps to conduct research. Record information on the Research Notes pages that follow. Use one page per source.

1. Read the research questions that you need to answer in your presentation about a historical figure:

    a. Where was the person born? What was the person's childhood like?

    b. What was the person's main accomplishment? What did that person do to achieve that accomplishment?

    c. What events affected the person's life and accomplishments? Did he or she face any obstacles? Did he or she make any mistakes?

    d. What is the person's legacy, or influence on life today?

    e. What are some fun facts about the person or quotes the person said?

2. Identify at least three sources (digital, print, or both) that you can use to answer the research questions. Record the title, author, publisher, and URL of each source on the Research Notes pages that follow. Use one page per source.

3. As you read each source, take notes on the Research Notes pages related to the research questions.

    - Label each fact with the letter of the question that it answers.
    - Write your notes in your own words.
    - If you find a direct quotation that you think you might use in your presentation, record the quotation, word for word, in quotation marks. Also record the name of the person you are quoting.

Research Notes

Source

Title: _____

Author: _____

Published by: _____

URL (if necessary): _____

Notes

Key Information Written in Your Own Words:

_____
_____
_____
_____
_____

Direct Quotations:

_____
_____
_____

Person Quoted: _____

Research Notes

Source

Title: _____

Author: _____

Published by: _____

URL (if necessary): _____

Notes

Key Information Written in Your Own Words:

_____
_____
_____
_____
_____
_____

Direct Quotations:

_____
_____
_____

Person Quoted: _____

PRESENTATION: RESEARCH

Research Notes

Source

Title: _____

Author: _____

Published by: _____

URL (if necessary): _____

Notes

Key Information Written in Your Own Words:

_____
_____
_____
_____
_____
_____

Direct Quotations:

_____
_____
_____

Person Quoted: _____

Reflect on your research.

4. What general conclusions can you draw from your research? Summarize your research in one to two sentences.

   _____
   _____
   _____
   _____

5. Look back at the research questions.

   a. How well does your research answer each question?

      _____
      _____
      _____
      _____

   b. Did you answer any questions in addition to the research questions? If so, what?

      _____
      _____
      _____

   c. Based on your research, list what you believe will be the topic of each body slide in your presentation.

      _____
      _____
      _____

GET READY

"The Value of Money"

Spelling List 26 Pretest

1. Open the Spelling Pretest activity online. Listen to the first spelling word. Type the word. Check your answer.

2. Write the correct spelling of the word in the Word column of the Spelling Pretest table on the next page.

	Word	✓	✗
1	blindfold		

3. Put a check mark in the ✓ column if you spelled the word correctly online.

	Word	✓	✗
1	blindfold	✓	

Put an X in the ✗ column if you spelled the word incorrectly online.

	Word	✓	✗
1	blindfold		✗

4. Repeat Steps 1–3 for the remaining words in the Spelling Pretest.

"The Value of Money"

Spelling List 26 Pretest

Write each spelling word in the Word column, making sure to spell it correctly.

	Word	✓	✗
1			
2			
3			
4			
5			
6			
7			
8			
9			

	Word	✓	✗
10			
11			
12			
13			
14			
15			
16			
17			

TRY IT
"The Value of Money"

Write About Two Texts

Respond in complete sentences.

Compare the structure of "The Value of Money" to the structure of another text in this unit. How are the two texts organized in similar ways? How are they organized differently? Cite details from the texts to support your points.

GET READY

"The Value of Money" Wrap-Up

Spelling List 26 Activity Bank

Circle any words in the box that you did not spell correctly on the pretest. Using your circled words, complete one activity of your choice. Complete as much of the activity as you can in the time given.

If you spelled all words correctly on the pretest, complete your chosen activity with as many spelling words as you can.

desert	formally	morality	proceed	automobile
dessert	formerly	mortality	hoard	mobility
envelop	flaunt	precede	horde	mobilize
envelope	flout			

Spelling Activity Choices

Silly Sentencess

1. Write a silly sentence using your words from the spelling word list.

2. Underline the spelling word in each sentence.
   Example: The dog was driving a car.

3. Correct any spelling errors.

Spelling Story

1. Write a very short story using your words from the spelling word list.

2. Underline the spelling words in the story.

3. Correct any spelling errors.

Riddle Me This

1. Write a riddle for your words from the spelling word list.
   Example: "I have a trunk, but it's not on my car."

2. Write the answer, which is your word, for each riddle.
   Example: Answer: elephant

3. Correct any spelling errors.

RunOnWord

1. Gather some crayons, colored pencils, or markers. Write each of your words, using a different color for each word, end to end as one long word.
   Example: dogcatbirdfishturtle

2. Rewrite the words correctly and with proper spacing.

- **Complete the activity that you chose.**

  My chosen activity: _____

TRY IT

"The Value of Money" Wrap-Up

Write About "The Value of Money"

Respond in complete sentences.

Think about what you read in "The Value of Money" and at least one other text in this unit. Briefly describe what these texts taught you. Finally, write about the most important thing you learned about money. Use details from the texts in your response.

_____
_____
_____
_____
_____
_____
_____
_____
_____

Can I barter for some popcorn?

TRY IT
"The Future of Money"

Write About Different Structures

Respond in complete sentences.

Describe the structure of each text listed below. Then explain why you think the writer chose to organize each work as he or she did.

"From Barter to Bitcoin":

_____
_____
_____
_____
_____
_____

"Making Money":

_____
_____
_____
_____
_____
_____

"The Value of Money":
_____
_____
_____
_____
_____

"The Future of Money":
_____
_____
_____
_____
_____

TRY IT

"The Future of Money" Wrap-Up

Write About What You've Read

Respond in complete sentences.

1. Think about the different text structures you've learned about in this unit. You've read articles in *Money, Money, Money* that organize ideas using chronological order, problem and solution, cause and effect, and compare and contrast. Each article also included several text features, such as headings, graphs, charts, diagrams, and illustrations.

   - Which article was your favorite? Why?
   - Which text feature was your favorite? Why?
   - Cite specific examples from the text in your response.

2. Compare and contrast the structure and text features of an article in *Money, Money, Money* to the structure and text features in another informational text you've read in this course.

   - How are the pieces similar? How are they different?
   - Considering its structure and text features, which text do you think is more effective?

   _____
   _____
   _____
   _____
   _____
   _____
   _____
   _____

TRY IT
Sayings

Apply: Use Common Sayings

Read the saying. Write a sentence or sentences that use the saying. The first one has been done for you.

1. Saying: **The leopard cannot change his spots.**

   Danny knew not to eat the candy on the counter. But he has a major sweet tooth, and the **leopard cannot change his spots**, so he gobbled up the sweets right away.

2. Saying: **Let sleeping dogs lie.**

   _____
   _____
   _____

3. Saying: **Live and let live.**

   _____
   _____
   _____

4. Saying: **Nothing ventured, nothing gained.**

   _____
   _____
   _____

5. Saying: **Old habits die hard.**

_____
_____
_____

6. Saying: **Once bitten, twice shy.**

_____
_____
_____

7. Saying: **The grass is always greener on the other side.**

_____
_____
_____

8. Saying: **Strike while the iron is hot.**

_____
_____
_____

GET READY

Meet Sherlock Holmes (A)

Spelling List 27 Pretest

1. Open the Spelling Pretest activity online. Listen to the first spelling word. Type the word. Check your answer.

2. Write the correct spelling of the word in the Word column of the Spelling Pretest table on the next page.

	Word	✓	✗
1	blindfold		

3. Put a check mark in the ✓ column if you spelled the word correctly online.

	Word	✓	✗
1	blindfold	✓	

Put an X in the ✗ column if you spelled the word incorrectly online.

	Word	✓	✗
1	blindfold		✗

4. Repeat Steps 1–3 for the remaining words in the Spelling Pretest.

Meet Sherlock Holmes (A)

Spelling List 27 Pretest

Write each spelling word in the Word column, making sure to spell it correctly.

	Word	✓	✗
1			
2			
3			
4			
5			
6			
7			
8			
9			

	Word	✓	✗
10			
11			
12			
13			
14			
15			
16			
17			

TRY IT

Meet Sherlock Holmes (A)

Draw a Conclusion

Answer the questions in complete sentences.

1. Based on Part 1 of "The Red-Headed League," what conclusion can you draw regarding whom Holmes is suspicious of in this story?

   _____
   _____

2. Which details or evidence from the text support your conclusion? Remember to quote accurately from the story.

   _____
   _____
   _____
   _____

GET READY

Meet Sherlock Holmes (B)

Spelling List 27 Activity Bank

Circle any words in the box that you did not spell correctly on the pretest. Using your circled words, complete one activity of your choice. Complete as much of the activity as you can in the time given.

If you spelled all words correctly on the pretest, complete your chosen activity with as many spelling words as you can.

tear	moped	moderate	refuse	present
content	dove	lead	separate	produce
contract	invalid	record	wound	sewer
convict	minute			

Spelling Activity Choices

Hidden Words

1. Draw a picture and "hide" as many words from the Spelling Word List inside the picture as you can.
2. See if others can find the words within the picture.

Triangle Spelling

Write each word in a triangle.

Ghost Words

1. Use a white crayon to write each spelling word.
2. Go over the white crayon writing with a colored marker.

Complete the activity that you chose.

My chosen activity: _____

458 MEET SHERLOCK HOLMES (B)

TRY IT

Meet Sherlock Holmes (B)

Write About a Different Narrator

Answer the question in complete sentences.

Dr. Watson is the narrator of "The Red-Headed League." But imagine that Holmes told the story. How would this tale be different if Holmes were the narrator?

TRY IT

Meet Sherlock Holmes (C)

Write About the Texts and Make a Prediction

Answer the questions in complete sentences.

1. How is "The Adventure of the Blue Carbuncle" similar to "The Red-Headed League"?

   _____
   _____
   _____
   _____

2. Based on what you know about Holmes and based on what happened in "The Red-Headed League," what do you think will happen in the rest of "The Adventure of the Blue Carbuncle"? Write down your prediction and provide support for it with details from the text.

   _____
   _____
   _____
   _____
   _____

TRY IT
Meet Sherlock Holmes (D)

Write a Summary of the Story

Respond in complete sentences.

Write a summary of "The Adventure of the Blue Carbuncle." Remember to include key details, describe events in the proper order, and include the story's most important theme(s).

GET READY
Meet Sherlock Holmes (E)

Spelling List 28 Pretest

1. Open the Spelling Pretest activity online. Listen to the first spelling word. Type the word. Check your answer.

2. Write the correct spelling of the word in the Word column of the Spelling Pretest table on the next page.

	Word	✓	✗
1	blindfold		

3. Put a check mark in the ✓ column if you spelled the word correctly online.

	Word	✓	✗
1	blindfold	✓	

Put an X in the ✗ column if you spelled the word incorrectly online.

	Word	✓	✗
1	blindfold		X

4. Repeat Steps 1–3 for the remaining words in the Spelling Pretest.

Meet Sherlock Holmes (E)

Spelling List 28 Pretest

Write each spelling word in the Word column, making sure to spell it correctly.

	Word	✓	✗
1			
2			
3			
4			
5			
6			
7			
8			
9			
10			
11			

	Word	✓	✗
12			
13			
14			
15			
16			
17			
18			
19			
20			
21			

TRY IT

Meet Sherlock Holmes (E)

Plan Your Own Graphic Mystery Story

Write a Sherlock Holmes story using both text and pictures. Respond to the questions to plan your story.

1. What crime will happen in your story? Describe the case that Holmes will have to solve.

   _____
   _____
   _____
   _____
   _____

2. Who will be the characters in your story? Describe them now.

   _____
   _____
   _____
   _____
   _____

3. Where and when will your story take place? Describe the setting now.

_____
_____
_____

4. How will Holmes solve the case? Describe the plot now.

_____
_____
_____
_____
_____
_____
_____
_____
_____
_____

I imagine my graphic novel as a comic strip.

GET READY

Meet Sherlock Holmes (F)

Spelling List 28 Activity Bank

Circle any words in the box that you did not spell correctly on the pretest. Using your circled words, complete one activity of your choice. Complete as much of the activity as you can in the time given.

If you spelled all words correctly on the pretest, complete your chosen activity with as many spelling words as you can.

billboard	countdown	headquarters	sweetheart	boredom
landscape	driveway	jackknives	teammate	stardom
drawbridge	foolproof	skyscraper	woodpecker	freedom
bookkeeper	furthermore	suitcase	seashore	wisdom
checkbook				

Spelling Activity Choices

Create a Crossword

1. Write a word from your spelling word list in the center of the grid paper.

2. Write another spelling word going across and sharing a letter with the first word. See how many words you can connect.

   Example:

		p				
	k	i	s	s	e	s
d		n				
r	o	c	k	s		
g						
s						

Word Search Puzzle

1. Draw a box on the grid paper. The box should be large enough to hold your words from the spelling word list.

2. Fill in the grid paper with words from your spelling list, writing them horizontally, vertically, and diagonally (forward and backward if you choose).

3. Fill in the rest of the box with random letters.

4. Ask someone to find and circle your spelling words in the puzzle you made.

Complete the activity that you chose.

My chosen activity: _____

MEET SHERLOCK HOLMES (F) **471**

TRY IT

Meet Sherlock Holmes (F)

Write a Graphic Mystery Story

Gather your completed Plan Your Own Graphic Mystery Story from Meet Sherlock Holmes (E). Use it to create a graphic novel that tells a Sherlock Holmes story using both text and pictures.

MEET SHERLOCK HOLMES (F) **473**

MEET SHERLOCK HOLMES (F) 475

TRY IT
Meet Sherlock Holmes (G)

Write About Your Reactions

Respond in complete sentences.

You have read two short stories, one graphic novel, and one play about Sherlock Holmes. Which of these four works did you like best? What did you like about it? How does the genre (category or type of literature) of the work—short story, graphic novel, play—affect your opinion of it?

_____
_____
_____
_____
_____
_____
_____
_____

TRY IT

Meet Sherlock Holmes (H)

Write About Listening to a Text

Respond in complete sentences.

In your opinion, what does hearing a text read aloud add to a story? Why is listening to a text such as "The Adventure of the Three Students" worthwhile?

_____
_____
_____
_____
_____
_____
_____

TRY IT
Meet Sherlock Holmes Wrap-Up

Write About Sherlock Holmes

Respond in complete sentences.

It has been more than 130 years since Sherlock Holmes first appeared in a story by Sir Arthur Conan Doyle. In addition to being the hero of more than 50 stories written by Doyle, Holmes has also been a central character in many plays, movies, television shows, and games. Why do you think Sherlock Holmes remains so popular? What is it about him that people still find appealing after all this time? Your answer should include at least one reason that explains why he remains popular and one supporting detail that explains why people still find him appealing.

_____
_____
_____
_____
_____
_____
_____

I wonder what characters will still be popular 100 years from today.

TRY IT

Presentation: Revising

Revise Your Informational Presentation

Use the checklist as you revise your informational presentation about a historical figure.

Content

- ☐ Introduction: Will the introduction capture the audience's attention?
- ☐ Introduction: Does the introduction state my main idea clearly?
- ☐ Body: Do the headings capture the main idea of each slide?
- ☐ Body: Do I provide enough facts I found during research to support the main idea of each slide?
- ☐ Body: Do I use sensory details to paint a picture with words?
- ☐ Body: Are all the facts and sensory details relevant to the main idea of the presentation?
- ☐ Conclusion: Does the conclusion restate my main idea?
- ☐ Sources: Do I list three trustworthy research sources?
- ☐ Media: Does the media I chose support the main idea of each slide?
- ☐ Media: Have I included the URL for any media that I found online?

Organization

☐ Does the introduction state my supporting ideas in the order they are presented in the body slides?

☐ Does the order of the body slides make sense?

☐ Do the bullets support the main idea of each slide? Should any bullets be moved to a different slide?

☐ Are the bullets in the same order in which I talk about them in the audio?

TRY IT

Presentation: Proofreading

Proofread Your Informational Presentation

Use the checklist to proofread the text and speech in your informational presentation about a historical figure. The items listed under Grammar and Usage apply to both text and speech.

Grammar and Usage

- ☐ Are all sentences complete and correct?
- ☐ Are there any missing or extra words?
- ☐ Are there sentences that can be combined to show how ideas relate?
- ☐ Are there sentences that can be expanded with additional details?
- ☐ Are there sentences that can be reduced to get rid of words that are not needed?
- ☐ Can any sentences be combined, expanded, or reduced to increase audience interest?
- ☐ Is the language appropriately formal or informal?
- ☐ Are there other grammatical or usage errors?

Mechanics

☐ Is every word spelled correctly, including frequently confused words?

☐ Does every sentence begin with a capital letter and end with the appropriate punctuation?

☐ Are the titles of works in the source list capitalized and formatted correctly?

☐ Are there other punctuation or capitalization errors?

Speech

☐ Do I speak at an appropriate pace? Are there any times I speak too quickly or too slowly?

☐ Do I speak clearly? Are there any words that I pronounce incorrectly?

☐ Do I speak at an appropriate volume?

TRY IT

Presentation: Publishing

Reflect on Your Informational Presentation

Refer to your informational presentation about a historical figure as you answer the questions.

1. Imagine you could share your presentation with anyone. Who would be your audience? Why? Be specific.

   _____
   _____
   _____

   a. How would you change the language in your presentation for your audience? Would you use any different words? Would you combine, expand, or reduce any sentences? Give at least one example.

   _____
   _____
   _____
   _____

   b. How would you change the examples or the media in your presentation for you audience? Would your audience relate better to different examples or media? Give at least one example.

   _____
   _____
   _____
   _____

2. In one sentence, state the purpose of your presentation.

_____
_____

a. Suppose you wanted to publish your presentation. Where could you try to publish your presentation?

   Note: Because of potential media copyright issues, do not actually publish your presentation.

   _____
   _____

b. Does your answer to Part A support the purpose of your presentation? Explain.

   _____
   _____

Glossary

academic word – a word used in educational settings more than in conversation; often a more precise word in place of a more common word

adage – an old, familiar saying that describes a common truth

adjective – a word that modifies, or describes, a noun or pronoun

affix – a word part attached to a root or base word to create a new word

alliteration – the use of words with the same or close to the same beginning sounds

allusion – a reference to a familiar literary or historical person or event, used to make an idea more easily understood

antonym – a word that means the opposite of another word

biography – the story of someone's life written by another person

book review – a piece of writing that gives an opinion about a book and tells about it

brainstorming – before writing, a way for the writer to come up with ideas

caption – text that tells more about an illustration, such as a photograph or other graphic

cause – the reason something happens

cause and effect – a situation in which one condition or fact, the cause, results in another, the effect

character – a person or animal in a story

character trait – a quality of a person or character; part of a personality

characterization – the techniques an author uses to reveal character traits; characters are revealed by their words, thoughts, actions, and what other characters say about them

chronological order – a way to organize that puts details in time order

claim – an idea or opinion presented, or a stand taken, in an argument

compare – to explain how two or more things are alike

compare-and-contrast organization – a structure for text that shows how two or more things are similar and different

complex sentence – a sentence that has one independent part and at least one dependent part

compound sentence – a sentence that has at least two independent parts

concluding sentence – the last sentence of a paragraph; it often summarizes the paragraph

conclusion – a decision made about something not stated, using information provided and what is already known

conclusion – the final paragraph of a written work

concrete – (adj.) real or physical; able to be perceived by the senses

conflict – a problem or issue that a character faces in a story

conjunction – a word used to join parts of a sentence, such as *and*, *but*, and *or*

consequence – what happens because of an action or event

context – the parts of a sentence or passage surrounding a word

context clue – a word or phrase in a text that helps you figure out the meaning of an unknown word

contrast – to explain how two or more things are different

coordinating conjunction – one of seven words—*and*, *but*, *for*, *nor*, *or*, *so*, *yet*—that connects words, phrases, or independent clauses

copyright – the right held by one person or company to publish, sell, distribute, and reproduce a work of art, literature, or music

correlative conjunction – one part of a pair of conjunctions that connects words or groups of words; example pairs: *either/or*, *neither/nor*, *both/and*

description – writing that uses words that show how something looks, sounds, feels, tastes, or smells
Example: The sky is a soft, powdery blue, and the golden sun feels warm on my face.

detail – a fact or description that tells more about a topic

diagram – a drawing or design that shows how pieces of information are related

dialect – a way of speaking that is particular to a certain group of people, place, or time

dialogue – the words that characters say in a written work

direct address – calling a person or animal by name or title; for example, "Look, Mary, I found it!" or "Doctor, come here."

direct quotation – the exact words of a speaker or writer

draft – an early effort at a piece of writing, not the finished work

drafting – of writing, the stage or step in which the writer first writes the piece

drama – another word for *play*

editorial – an article in a publication that gives an opinion held by its editor or editors; an opinion piece similar to such an article

effect – the result of a cause

evidence – a specific detail, such as a fact or expert opinion, that supports a reason

fact – something that can be proven true

figurative language – words that describe something by comparing it to something completely different
Example: Rain fell in buckets and the streets looked like rivers.

firsthand account – an account told from direct personal experience or observation

first-person narrator – a narrator who tells a story from the first-person point of view

first-person point of view – the telling of a story by a character in that story, using pronouns such as *I*, *me*, and *we*

formal language – the choice of words, phrases, and sentences that adhere to the conventional standards of grammar, usage, and mechanics

fragment – an incomplete sentence that begins with a capital letter and ends with a punctuation mark

free verse – poetry whose rhythm follows natural speech patterns and does not rely on regular rhyme or meter

future perfect tense – verb tense that shows an action that will be completed in the future before another action happens

future progressive tense – verb tense that shows an ongoing action that has not yet happened
Example: I will be swimming most days this summer.

glossary – a list of important terms and their meanings that is usually found in the back of a book

graph – a pictorial way to display data

graphic – a picture, photograph, map, diagram, or other image

graphic organizer – a visual device, such as a diagram or chart, that helps a writer plan a piece of writing

heading – a title within the body of a text that tells the reader something important about a section of the text

helping verb – a word that works with the main verb to show action; for example, *has*, *have*, *will*, *do*, *did*, *can*

historical fiction – a story set in a historical time period that includes facts about real people, places, and events, but also contains fictional elements that add dramatic interest to the story

homograph – a word that has the same spelling as another word but has a different pronunciation and meaning

homonym – a word that is spelled the same and sounds the same but has a different meaning from another word

homophone – a word that sounds the same as another word but has a different spelling and meaning

hook – a surprising idea or group of words used to grab the reader's attention, usually at the beginning of a work

idiom – a group of words that does not actually mean what it says
Examples: raining cats and dogs; a month of Sundays

imagery – language that helps readers imagine how something looks, sounds, smells, feels, or tastes

infer – to use clues and what you already know to make a guess

inference – a guess that readers make using the clues that an author gives them in a piece of writing

informal language – language that may include, for example, personal feeling, slang, contractions, humor, and fragments

informational essay – a kind of writing that informs or explains

informational text – text written to explain and give information on a topic

interjection – a word (or words) that expresses strong feeling

Internet – a global communications system of linked computer networks

introduction – the first paragraph of an essay, identifying the topic and stating the main idea

legend – a story that is passed down for many years to teach the values of a culture; a legend may or may not contain some true events or people

line – a row of words in a poem

main idea – the most important point the author makes; it may be stated or unstated

mass media – communication—such as television, movies, radio, and newspapers—designed to reach many, or the mass of, people

media – all the ways by which something can be shown, shared, or expressed

metaphor – a figure of speech that compares two unlike things, without using the word *like* or *as*
Example: The cat's eyes were emeralds shining in the night.

meter – the arrangement of words in poetry based on rhythm, accents, and the number of syllables in a line

mood – the emotions or feelings conveyed in a literary work

narrative – a kind of writing that tells a story

narrative nonfiction – a story based on fact, told using the same kind of plan and features that fictional stories use

narrative poem – a poem that tells a story

narrator – the teller of a story

nonfiction – writing that presents facts and information to explain, describe, or persuade; for example, newspaper articles and biographies are nonfiction

nuance – a very small difference in meaning

onomatopoeia – the use of words that show sounds, such as the words *moo, woof, quack, squash*

opinion – something that a person thinks or believes, but which cannot be proven to be true

outline – an organized list of topics in an essay

pace/pacing (in speech) – the speed, and the change of speeds, of a speaker's delivery

pace/pacing (in writing) – the speed at which events unfold or information is revealed in a narrative

paraphrase – to restate information in one's own words

past perfect tense – verb tense that shows an action that was completed before another action happened

past progressive tense – verb tense that shows an ongoing action that already happened
Example: I was sleeping earlier.

personal narrative – an essay about a personal experience of the writer

personification – giving human qualities to something that is not human
Example: The thunder shouted from the clouds.

perspective – the way someone sees the world

persuasive essay – an essay in which the writer tries to convince readers to agree with a stance on an issue

plagiarism – use of another person's words without giving that person credit as a source

plot – what happens in a story; the sequence of events

poem – a piece of poetry

point of view – the perspective a story is told from

precise language – language that is specific and exact

predicate – the verb or verb phrase in a sentence

prediction – a guess about what might happen that is based on information in a story and what you already know

prefix – a word part with its own meaning that can be added to the beginning of a base word or root to make a new word with a different meaning

preposition – a word that begins a phrase that ends with a noun or pronoun
Examples: In the phrases "over the bridge" and "to me," the words *over* and *to* are prepositions.

prepositional phrase – a group of words that begins with a preposition and usually ends with the noun or a pronoun that is the object of the preposition

present perfect tense – verb tense that shows an action that either (1) happened at a vague time in the past or (2) started in the past and has continued into the present

present progressive tense – verb tense that shows an ongoing action that is happening now
Example: I am eating breakfast right now.

prewriting – the stage or step of writing in which a writer chooses a topic, gathers ideas, and plans what to write

primary source – a record made by a person who saw or took part in an event or who lived at the time

problem (literature) – an issue a character must solve in a story

problem-solution structure (writing) – organizational pattern in which a problem is described, followed by descriptions of its solution or possible solutions

proofreading – the stage or step of the writing process in which the writer checks for errors in grammar, punctuation, capitalization, and spelling

proper adjective – an adjective form of a proper noun; for example, *European* or *Japanese*

proper noun – a noun that names a particular person, place, thing, or idea

prose – the form of written language without the rhyme, rhythm, and meter that the language of poetry has

proverb – a brief, popular saying that describes a wise thought

publishing – the stage or step of the writing process in which the writer makes a clean copy of the piece and shares it

reason – a statement that explains why something is or why it should be

relative adverb – one of the three adverbs *when*, *where*, and *why* that relates an adjective clause to the noun or pronoun the clause describes

relative pronoun – a pronoun that relates an adjective clause to the noun or pronoun the clause describes

repetition – repeating words or phrases

research – to find information through study rather than through personal experience

resolution – the outcome of a story

revising – the stage or step of the writing process in which the writer rereads and edits the draft, correcting errors and making changes in content or organization that improve the piece

rhyme – the use of words that end with the same sounds; for example, *cat* and *hat* rhyme

rhyme scheme – the pattern of rhymes made by the last sounds in the lines of a poem, shown by a different letter of the alphabet to represent each rhyme

rhythm (poetry) – a regular pattern of sound and beats within a poem

root – a word part with a special meaning to which prefixes and suffixes can be added; for example, *spec* is a root that means "see"

run-on – two or more sentences that have been joined without a conjunction or proper punctuation

scene (drama) – a subdivision of an act of a play that happens at a fixed time and place

scientific method – a way to find answers by experimenting, observing, and drawing conclusions

secondary source – a record made by a person who did not see or take part in an event, or who made the record later

secondhand account – an account told through research rather than by way of direct personal experience or observation

sensory detail – descriptive detail that appeals to any of the senses—sight, hearing, touch, smell, or taste

sensory language – language that appeals to the five senses

sentence – a group of words that tells a complete thought

sequence – the order in which things happen

sequence of events (plot) – what happens in a story; the plot

setting – where and when a literary work takes place

simile – a comparison between two things using the words *like* or *as*
Example: I didn't hear him come in because he was as quiet as a mouse.

simple sentence – a sentence that is one independent clause

source – a provider of information; a book, a historical document, online materials, and an interviewee are all sources

speaker – the imaginary person who speaks the words of a poem, not the poet

stage directions – instructions from a playwright that tell the actors what to do during the play

stanza – a group of lines in a poem

structure (writing) – the way a piece of writing is organized

style – the words a writer chooses and the way the writer arranges the words into sentences

subject – a word or words that tell whom or what the sentence is about

subordinating conjunction – a word that is used to introduce a dependent clause

suffix – a word part added to the end of a base word or root that changes the meaning or part of speech of a word

summarize (informational text) – to restate briefly the main points of a text

summarize (literary text: story, play, poem) – to tell in order the most important ideas or events of a text

summary – a short retelling that includes only the most important ideas or events of a text

supporting detail – a detail that gives more information about a main idea

suspense – uncertainty about what will happen

syllable – a unit of spoken language; a syllable contains only one vowel sound

synonym – a word that means the same, or almost the same, as another word

tag question – a question, or tag, added to a statement to engage the listener; for example: It's nice out, isn't it?

text feature – part of a text that helps a reader locate information and determine what is most important; some examples are the title, table of contents, headings, pictures, and glossary

theme – the author's message or big idea

thesis statement – the sentence that states the main idea of an essay

third-person point of view – the telling of a story by someone outside of the action, using the third-person pronouns *he*, *she*, and *they*

time order (sequential) organizational structure – the arrangement of ideas according to when they happened

tone (literature) – the author's feelings toward the subject or characters of a text

tone (speaking) – a speaker's attitude as shown by his or her voice

topic – the subject of a text

topic sentence – the sentence that expresses the main idea of a paragraph

transition – a word, phrase, or clause that connects ideas

transitional word or phrase – a word or phrase, such as *for example*, used to move from one idea to another

viewpoint (related to point of view) – the perspective of a person or group

visual (n.) – a graphic, picture, or photograph

visualization – the picturing of something in one's mind

visualize – to picture things in your mind as you read

website – a place on the Internet devoted to a specific organization, group, or individual

writing prompt – a sentence or sentences that ask for a particular kind of writing